WHO WROTE THAT?

(PT 5)

Gina C. Wilson
St. Mary's College,
Cheltenham

PTARMIGAN BOOKS

WHO WROTE THAT?

Compiled by

HUBERT PHILLIPS

PENGUIN BOOKS

WEST DRAYTON MIDDLESEX

First Published in 1948
by PENGUIN BOOKS, Harmondsworth, Middlesex.

Made and Printed in Great Britain for Penguin Books Limited
by Hunt, Barnard and Co., Ltd., London and Aylesbury

FOREWORD

★

WHO WROTE THAT? is, in a specialised sense, a Quiz. The reader is offered four hundred "quotations", arranged in forty groups of ten each. Each group can be made the basis either of an oral test—with a Compère reading out the Quotations—or of a pencil-and-paper game. Or, of course, the solitary reader can have fun testing himself.

I have always maintained that there is no point in any kind of Quiz unless the questions asked are of interest in themselves. With quotations from well-known authors—if they are reasonably well selected—one is here on very safe ground. It is always worth knowing whence a familiar "tag", or a passage that has given especial pleasure, is derived. Nor is that all. A quotation may serve to remind the reader of some half-forgotten book or poem, and send him back to it with renewed interest in the author and his work. Or it may serve to introduce him to writers who, hitherto, have only been names to him; or of whom, even, he may not have heard at all.

During the war years reading was very much on the down grade. Many of us were inevitably separated—some of us are still separated—from our books. Millions of the best books were destroyed by enemy action. Paper has long been "in short supply". The object of this little book is simply to provide entertainment; but a glance through its contents may serve too as a reminder that we have an indestructible literature.

I make no apology for the fact that the majority of my quotations are well known—some of them very well-known indeed. A Quiz should serve to give pleasure to those who take part in it: it is not an examination. Even so, any reader who can, at sight, name the authors of, say, seven passages out of ten, may reasonably award himself Distinction.

H. P.

JUNE, 1947.

1. ALL'S WELL

The year's at the spring,
And day's at the morn;
Morning's at seven;
The hill-side's dew-pearled;
The lark's on the wing;
The snail's on the thorn:
God's in his heaven—
All's right with the world.

2. PERFIDY

Cosmus duke of Florence, was wont to say of perfidious friends; "That we read that we ought to forgive our enemies; but we do not read that we ought to forgive our friends."

3. THIEF

Procrastination is the thief of time.

4. A CHANGED WORLD

It is now sixteen or seventeen years since I saw the Queen of France, then the Dauphiness, at Versailles; and surely never lighted on this orb, which she hardly seemed to touch, a more delightful vision. I saw her just above the horizon, decorating and cheering the elevated sphere she just began to move in—glittering like the morning star, full of life, and splendour, and joy . . . Little did I dream that I should have lived to see disasters fallen upon her in a nation of gallant men, in a nation of men of honour, and of cavaliers. I thought ten thousand swords must have leaped from their scabbards to avenge even a look that threatened her with insult. But the age of chivalry is gone. That of sophisters, economists, and calculators, has succeeded; and the glory of Europe is extinguished for ever.

5.   MORTIFYING

I confess freely to you, I could never look long upon a monkey, without very mortifying reflections.

6.   LIFE

The One remains, the many change and pass;
Heaven's light forever shines, Earth's shadows fly;
Life, like a dome of many-coloured glass,
Stains the white radiance of Eternity.

7.   WHERE IGNORANCE IS BLISS

Yet ah! why should they know their fate?
Since sorrow never comes too late,
    And happiness too swiftly flies.
Thought would destroy their paradise.
No more; where ignorance is bliss,
    'Tis folly to be wise.

8. FIRST LOVE

All the girls are out with their baskets for the primrose;
    Up lanes, woods through, they troop in joyful bands.
My sweet leads: she knows not why, but now she
      loiters,
    Eyes the bent anemones, and hangs her hands.
Such a look will tell that the violets are peeping,
    Coming the rose: and unaware a cry
Springs in her bosom for odours and for colour,
    Covert and the nightingale; she knows not why.

9. THRENODY

    Fear no more the heat o' the sun,
      Nor the furious winter's rages;
    Thou thy worldly task hast done,
      Home art gone and ta'en thy wages:
    Golden lads and girls all must,
    As chimney-sweepers, come to dust.

10. LAST JOURNEY

Sunset and evening star,
    And one clear call for me!
And may there be no moaning of the bar,
    When I put out to sea,

But such a tide as moving seems asleep,
    Too full for sound and foam,
When that which drew from out the boundless deep
    Turns again home.

1. THE GODS OF HELLAS

Saturn and Love their long repose
    Shall burst, more bright and good
Than all who fell, than One who rose,
    Than many unsubdued;
Not gold, not blood, their altar dowers,
But votive tears and symbol flowers.

2. MUSIC

If music be the food of love, play on;
Give me excess of it, that, surfeiting,
The appetite may sicken, and so die.
That strain again! it had a dying fall:
O! it came o'er my ear like the sweet sound
That breathes upon a bank of violets,
Stealing and giving odour! Enough! no more.

3. THE SUNFLOWER

Ah, Sun-flower! weary of time,
Who countest the steps of the Sun;
Seeking after that sweet golden clime,
Where the traveller's journey is done;

Where the Youth pined away with desire,
And the pale Virgin shrouded in snow,
Arise from their graves and aspire
Where my Sun-flower wishes to go.

4. BLESSED DAMOZEL

The blessèd damozel leaned out
    From the gold bar of Heaven;
Her eyes were deeper than the depth
    Of waters stilled at even;
She had three lilies in her hand,
    And the stars in her hair were seven.

5. A WISH

I wish I loved the Human Race;
I wish I loved its silly face;
I wish I liked the way it walks;
I wish I liked the way it talks;
And when I'm introduced to one
I wish I thought *What Jolly Fun*!

6. THE WARM SOUTH

O, for a draught of vintage! that hath been
Cool'd a long age in the deep-delved earth,
Tasting of Flora and the country green,
Dance, and Provençal song, and sunburnt mirth!
O for a beaker full of the warm South,
Full of the true, the blushful Hippocrene,
With beaded bubbles winking at the brim,
And purple-stained mouth;
That I might drink, and leave the world unseen,
And with thee fade away into the forest dim.

7. SNUB

"Very well," cried I, "that's a good girl, I find you are perfectly qualified for making converts, and so go help your mother to make the gooseberry-pie."

8. ITALY

Italy, my Italy!
Queen Mary's saying serves for me—
  (When fortune's malice
  Lost her—Calais)
Open my heart and you will see
Graved inside of it, "Italy".

9. REALITY

Do you think that the things people make fools of themselves about are any less real and true than the things they behave sensibly about?

10. IN HIS FASHION

I have forgot much, Cynara! gone with the wind,
Flung roses, roses, riotously with the throng,
Dancing, to put thy pale lost lilies out of mind:
  But I was desolate and sick of an old passion,
Yes, all the time, because the dance was long:
  I have been faithful to thee, Cynara! in my fashion.

★

1. PATRIOT

"Here and here did England help me: how can I help
England?"—say,
Whoso turns as I, this evening, turn to God to praise
and pray,
While Jove's planet rises yonder, silent over Africa.

2. INNISFREE

I will arise and go now, for always night and day
I hear lake water lapping with low sounds by the shore;
While I stand on the roadway, or on the pavements
gray
I hear it in the deep heart's core.

3. YOU CAN ALWAYS TELL

You can always tell an old soldier by the inside of
his holsters and cartridge boxes   The young ones
carry pistols and cartridges; the old ones, grub.

4. LOOKING FORWARD

These things shall be! A loftier race
Than e'er the world hath known, shall rise,
With flame of freedom in their souls,
And light of knowledge in their eyes.

5. DRAKE

Drake he's in his hammock till the great Armadas
  come.
  (Capten, art tha sleepin' there below?)
Slung atween the round shot, listenin' for the drum,
  An' dreamin' arl the time o' Plymouth Hoe.
Call him on the deep sea, call him up the Sound,
  Call him when ye sail to meet the foe;
Where the old trade's plyin' an' the old flag flyin'
  They shall find him ware an' wakin', as they found
    him long ago!

6. FIRST THINGS FIRST

If a madman were to come into this room with a
stick in his hand, no doubt we should pity the state
of his mind; but our primary consideration would be
to take care of ourselves. We should knock him down
first, and pity him afterwards.

7. WHAT'S IN A NAME?

Call me Sappho, call me Chloris,
Call me Lalage or Doris,
  Only, only call me thine.

8. EURIPIDES

Our Euripides, the human,
With his droppings of warm tears,
And his touches of things common
Till they rose to touch the spheres!

8

9.   LIFE IS REAL

Life is real! Life is earnest!
   And the grave is not its goal;
Dust thou art, to dust returnest,
   Was not spoken of the soul.

10.   SPRING TIME

It was a lover and his lass,
   With a hey, and a ho, and a hey nonino,
That o'er the green cornfield did pass,
   In the spring time, the only pretty ring time,
When birds do sing, hey ding a ding, ding;
Sweet lovers love the spring.

1. MUSIC MAKERS

We are the music makers
   And we are the dreamers of dreams,
Wandering by lone sea-breakers,
   And sitting by desolate streams:—
World-losers and world-forsakers,
   On whom the pale moon gleams:
We are the movers and shakers
   Of the world for ever, it seems.

2. THE CAREERIST

A man may speak very well in the House of
Commons, and fail very completely in the House of
Lords. There are two distinct styles requisite; I
intend, in the course of my career, if I have time, to
give a specimen of both.

3. BRITANNIA

When Britain first, at heaven's command,
Arose from out the azure main,
This was the charter of the land,
And guardian angels sung this strain:
   "Rule, Britannia, rule the waves;
   "Britons never will be slaves."

4. THE GULL'S WAY

I must down to the seas again, to the vagrant gypsy life,
To the gull's way and the whale's way where the
    wind's like a whetted knife;
And all I ask is a merry yarn from a laughing fellow-
    rover,
And quiet sleep and a sweet dream when the long
    trick's over.

5. THE LOVER

Shall I compare thee to a summer's day?
Thou art more lovely and more temperate:
Rough winds do shake the darling buds of May,
And summer's lease hath all too short a date:
Sometime too hot the eye of heaven shines,
And often is his gold complexion dimm'd;
And every fair from fair sometime declines,
By chance, or nature's changing course untrimm'd;
But thy eternal summer shall not fade,
Nor lose possession of that fair thou ow'st,
Nor shall death brag thou wander'st in his shade,
When in eternal lines to time thou grow'st;
So long as men can breathe, or eyes can see,
So long lives this, and this gives life to thee.

6. THEY DIED IN BATTLE

Blow out, you bugles, over the rich Dead!
    There's none of these so lonely and poor of old,
    But, dying, has made us rarer gifts than gold.

These laid the world away; poured out the red
Sweet wine of youth; gave up the years to be
 Of work and joy, and that unhoped serene,
 That men call age; and those who would have been
Their sons, they gave, their immortality.

7. WHO KNOWS?

To be, or not to be: that is the question:
Whether 'tis nobler in the mind to suffer
The slings and arrows of outrageous fortune,
Or to take arms against a sea of troubles,
And by opposing end them? To die; to sleep;
No more; and, by a sleep to say we end
The heart-ache and the thousand natural shocks
That flesh is heir to, 'tis a consummation
Devoutly to be wish'd.

8. A FANCY

I sometimes think that never blows so red
The Rose as where some buried Cæsar bled;
 That every Hyacinth the Garden wears
Dropt in her Lap from some once lovely Head.

9. TEA PARTY

"Take some more tea," the March Hare said to
Alice, very earnestly.

"I've had nothing yet," Alice replied in an
offended tone, "so I can't take more."

"You mean you can't take *less*," said the Hatter: "it's very easy to take *more* than nothing."

10. MARCHING ON

Mine eyes have seen the glory of the coming of the
     Lord:
He is trampling out the vintage where the grapes of
     wrath are stored;
He hath loosed the fatal lighting of his terrible swift
     sword:
    His truth is marching on.
I have seen him in the watch-fires of a hundred circling
     camps;
They have builded him an altar in the evening dews
     and damps;
I can read his righteous sentence by the dim and
     flaring lamps:
    His day is marching on.

1. ONE SONG, ONE ANGEL

Oh, their Rafael of the dear Madonnas,
Oh, their Dante of the dread Inferno,
Wrote one song—and in my brain I sing it,
Drew one angel—borne, see, on my bosom!

2. BETTER NOT ASK

Ask yourself whether you are happy, and you cease
to be so.

3. HONOUR

Yet this inconstancy is such,
As you too shall adore;
I could not love the, dear, so much,
Lov'd I not honour more.

4. THE RIGHT APPROACH

With malice toward none; with charity for all;
with firmness in the right, as God gives us to see the
right.

5. WORDS

Drive my dead thoughts over the universe
Like withered leaves to quicken a new birth!
And, by the incantation of this verse,

Scatter, as from an unextinguished hearth
Ashes and sparks, my words among mankind!

6 RECLUSE

For most, I know, thou lov'st retired ground.
　Thee, at the ferry, Oxford riders blithe,
　　Returning home on summer nights, have met
Crossing the stripling Thames at Bablock-hithe,
　　Trailing in the cool stream thy fingers wet,
　　　As the slow punt swings round:
And leaning backwards in a pensive dream,
　　And fostering in thy lap a heap of flowers
　　　Pluck'd in shy fields and distant Wychwood
　　　　bowers,
And thine eyes resting on the moonlit stream.

7. LIFE IS SWEET

There's night and day, brother, both sweet things;
sun, moon and stars, brother, all sweet things; there's
likewise a wind on the heath. Life is very sweet,
brother; who would wish to die?

8. A QUERY

What do we, as a nation, care about books? How
much do you think we spend altogether on our
libraries, public or private, as compared with what
we spend on our horses?

15

9. WHO ARE THESE?

Who are these coming to the sacrifice?
To what green altar, O mysterious priest,
Lead'st thou that heifer lowing at the skies,
And all her silken flanks with garlands drest?
What little town by river or sea shore,
Or mountain-built with peaceful citadel,
Is emptied of this folk, this pious morn?

10. SOME VILLAGE HAMPDEN

Some village Hampden, that with dauntless breast
  The little tyrant of his fields withstood;
Some mute inglorious Milton here may rest,
  Some Cromwell guiltless of his country's blood.

★

1. LAMENT

But, O the heavy change, now thou art gone,
Now thou art gone, and never must return!

2. BROOM AND HAWTHORN

Oh tarnish late on Wenlock Edge,
    Gold that I never see;
Lie long, high snowdrifts in the hedge,
    That will not shower on me.

3. A NIGHT FOR LOVE

    In such a night
Stood Dido with a willow in her hand
Upon the wild sea-banks, and waft her love
To come again to Carthage.

4. TO SHAKESPEARE

Lo, Shakespeare, since thy time nature is loth
To yield to art her fair supremacy;
In conquering one thou hast so enriched both.
What shall I say? for God—whose wise decree
Confirmeth all He did by all He doth—
Doubled His whole creation making thee.

17

5. THIS ABOVE ALL

This above all: to thine own self be true,
And it must follow, as the night the day,
Thou canst not then be false to any man.

6. A VISION

Was this the face that launch'd a thousand ships,
And burnt the topless towers of Ilium?
Sweet Helen, make me immortal with a kiss!

7. A SMILING FACE

I have a smiling face, she said,
   I have a jest for all I meet,
I have a garland for my head
   And all its flowers are sweet—
And so you call me gay, she said.

Grief taught to me this smile, she said,
   And Wrong did teach this jesting bold;
These flowers were pluck'd from garden-bed
   While a death-chime was toll'd.
And what now will you say?—she said.

8. UNDEFEATED

In the fell clutch of circumstance,
I have not winced nor cried aloud:
Under the bludgeonings of chance
My head is bloody, but unbowed.

9.   THE REASON

I must learn Spanish, one of these days,
Only for that slow sweet name's sake.

10.   GOOD MORROW

And now good morrow to our waking souls,
Which watch not one another out of fear.

★

1. DUST TO DUST

For dust thou art, and unto dust thou shalt return.

2. HEROES

How sleep the brave, who sink to rest,
By all their country's wishes blest!

3. WOMAN

I expect that Woman will be the last thing civilized
by Man.

4. WHAT IS HONOUR?

Honour pricks me on. Yea, but how if honour
prick me off when I come on? How then? Can honour
set-to a leg? No. Or an arm? No. Or take away
the grief of a wound? No. Honour hath no skill in
surgery, then? No. What is honour? A word. What
is that word, honour? Air. A trim reckoning!
Who hath it? He that died o' Wednesday. Doth he
feel it? No. Doth he hear it? No. It is insensible
then? Yea, to the dead. But will it not live with the
living? No. Why? Detraction will not suffer it.
Therefore I'll none of it: honour is a mere scutcheon:
and so ends my catechism.

5. TIRED

Tir'd with all these, for restful death I cry,
As to behold desert a beggar born,
And needy nothing trimm'd in jollity,
And purest faith unhappily forsworn,
And gilded honour shamefully misplac'd,
And maiden virtue rudely strumpeted,
And right perfection wrongfully disgrac'd,
And strength by limping sway disabled,
And art made tongue-tied by authority,
And folly—doctor-like—controlling skill,
And simple truth miscall'd simplicity,
And captive good attending captain ill:
Tir'd with all these, from these I would be gone,
Save that, to die, I leave my love alone.

6. HUMILITY

I dare not ask a kiss;
I dare not beg a smile;
Lest having that, or this,
I might grow proud the while.

No, no, the utmost share
Of my desire, shall be
Only to kiss that air,
That lately kissèd thee.

7. GOOD ADVICE

"The horror of that moment," the King went on,
"I shall never, *never* forget!" "You will, though,"
the Queen said, "if you don't make a memorandum
of it."

8. CALIBAN'S GOD

Setebos, Setebos, and Setebos!
'Thinketh, He dwelleth i' the cold o' the moon.
'Thinketh He made it, with the sun to match,
But not the stars; the stars came otherwise.

9. THE VERY SINEWS

Good company and good discourse are the very
sinews of virtue.

10. PAN

What was he doing, the great god Pan,
　　Down in the reeds by the river?
Spreading ruin and scattering ban,
Splashing and paddling with hoofs of a goat,
And breaking the golden lilies afloat
　　With the dragon-fly on the river.

★

1. A WARNING

Be sure your sin will find you out.

2. ILL NEWS

Ill news hath wings, and with the wind doth go,
Comfort's a cripple and comes ever slow.

3. MUSIC

Out of the cradle endlessly rocking,
Out of the mocking-bird's throat, the musical shuttle.

4. PHILOSOPHY

How charming is divine philosophy!
Not harsh, and crabbed as dull fools suppose,
But musical as is Apollo's lute,
And a perpetual feast of nectared sweets,
Where no crude surfeit reigns.

5. CRISPIAN'S DAY

This day is called the feast of Crispian;
He that outlives this day and comes safe home,
Will stand a tip-toe when this day is nam'd,
And rouse him at the name of Crispian.

6. AN ENGLISHMAN'S HOME

Go anywhere in England, where there are natural, wholesome, contented, and really nice English people; and what do you always find? That the stables are the real centre of the household.

7. ADVERSITY

Sweet are the uses of adversity,
Which like the toad, ugly and venomous,
Wears yet a precious jewel in his head;
And this our life, exempt from public haunt,
Finds tongues in trees, books in the running brooks,
Sermons in stones, and good in everything.

8. TAKE NOTE

The world's great men have not commonly been great scholars, nor its great scholars great men.

9. LOGIC

"I'm sure nobody walks much faster than I do!"
"He can't do that," said the King, "or else he'd have been here first."

10. IT'S SAFER

It's wiser being good than bad;
    It's safer being meek than fierce:
It's fitter being sane than mad.

My own hope is, a sun will pierce
The thickest cloud earth ever stretched;
That, after Last, returns the First,
Though a wide compass round be fetched;
That what began best can't end worst,
Nor what God blessed once, prove accurst.

1. PARADOX

Out of the eater came forth meat, and out of the strong came forth sweetness.

2. LAST SALUTE

And when Thyself with shining Foot shall pass
Among the Guests Star-scattered on the Grass,
    And in thy joyous Errand reach the Spot
Where I made one—turn down an empty Glass.

3. TOO LATE

For all sad words of tongue or pen,
The saddest are these: "It might have been".

4. SORROW

Yet once more, O ye laurels, and once more
Ye myrtles brown, with ivy never sere,
I come to pluck your berries harsh and crude,
And with forc'd fingers rude,
Shatter your leaves before the mellowing year.

I spake of most disastrous chances,
Of moving accidents by flood and field,
Of hair-breadth 'scapes i' the imminent deadly breach,
Of being taken by the insolent foe
And sold to slavery, of my redemption thence
And portance in my travel's history;
Wherein of antres vast and desarts idle,
Rough quarries, rocks and hills whose heads touch
   heaven,
It was my hint to speak, such was the process;
And of the Cannibals that each other eat,
The Anthropophagi, and men whose heads
Do grow beneath their shoulders.

6. NOSTRUM

I remember when our whole island was shaken
with an earthquake some years ago, there was an
impudent mountebank who sold pills which (as he
told the country people) were very good against an
earthquake.

7. THE LOVER

Break an hour's promise in love! He that will
divide a minute into a thousand parts, and break but a
part of the thousandth part of a minute in the affairs
of love, it may be said of him that Cupid hath clapped
him o' the shoulder, but I'll warrant him heart-whole.

8. THE MERCENARIES

These, in the day when heaven was falling,
   The hour when earth's foundations fled,
Followed their mercenary calling
   And took their wages and are dead.

Their shoulders held the sky suspended;
   They stood, and earth's foundations stay;
What God abandoned, these defended,
   And saved the sum of things for pay.

9. NIGHT PIECE

Her eyes the glow-worm lend thee,
The shooting-stars attend thee;
    And the elves also,
    Whose little eyes glow,
Like the sparks of fire, befriend thee.

No Will-o'-th'-Wisp mislight thee;
Nor snake, or slow-worm bite thee;
    But on, on thy way
    Not making a stay,
Since ghost there's none to affright thee.

10. THE MUSIC OF THE SPHERES

Sure there is music even in the beauty, and the
silent note which Cupid strikes, far sweeter than the

sound of an instrument. For there is a music where-
ever there is a harmony, order or proportion; and
thus far we may maintain the music of the spheres;
for those well ordered motions, and regular paces,
though they give no sound unto the ear, yet to the
understanding they strike a note most full of harmony.

★

1. A LITTLE CLOUD

There ariseth a little cloud out of the sea, like a man's hand.

2. THE OXEN

Christmas Eve, and twelve of the clock.
"Now they are all on their knees,"
An elder said as we sat in a flock
By the embers in hearthside ease.

3. SUCH FUN!

On an occasion of this kind it becomes more than a moral duty to speak one's mind. It becomes a pleasure.

4. A PORTRAIT

She is older than the rocks among which she sits; like the vampire, she has been dead many times, and learned the secrets of the grave; and has been a diver in deep seas, and keeps their fallen day about her; and trafficked for strange webs with Eastern merchants: and, as Leda, was the mother of Helen of Troy, and, as Saint Anne, the mother of Mary; and all this has been to her but as the sound of lyres and flutes, and lives only in the delicacy with which it has moulded the changing lineaments, and tinged the eyelids and the hands.

5. JERUSALEM

I give you the end of a golden string;
   Only wind it into a ball,
It will lead you in at Heaven's gate,
   Built in Jerusalem's wall.

6. MELANCHOLY

We look before and after;
  We pine for what is not;
Our sincerest laughter
  With some pain is fraught;
Our sweetest songs are those that tell of saddest
    thought.

7. A GOOD DEATH

  Nothing in his life
Became him like the leaving it; he died
As one that had been studied in his death
To throw away the dearest thing he owed
As 'twere a careless trifle.

8. DISCOVERY

Then I felt like some watcher of the skies
When a new planet swims into his ken;
Or like stout Cortez when with eagle eyes
He star'd at the Pacific—and all his men
Look'd at each other with a wild surmise—
Silent, upon a peak in Darien.

9. JOY IN HEAVEN

'Twould ring the bells of Heaven
The wildest peal for years,
If Parson lost his senses
And people came to theirs,
And he and they together
Knelt down with angry prayers
For tamed and shabby tigers
And dancing dogs and bears,
And wretched, blind, pit ponies,
And little hunted hares.

10. THE LITTLE BIRDS

Oh, the little birds sang east, and the little birds sang
west, Toll slowly.
And I smiled to think God's greatness flowed around
our incompleteness—
Round our restlessness, His rest.

1. GO TO THE ANT

Go to the ant, thou sluggard; consider her ways
and be wise.

2. PERFECTION

It is not growing like a tree
In bulk, doth make men better be;
Or standing long an oak, three hundred year,
To fall a log at last, dry, bald, and sere:
  A lily of a day,
  Is fairer far in May.
Although it fall and die that night;
It was the plant and flower of light.
In small proportions we just beauties see;
And in short measures, life may perfect be.

3. DUTY

Stern daughter of the voice of God!
O Duty! if that name thou love
Who art a light to guide, a rod
To check the erring and reprove.

4. REFLECTION

i see it is impossible for the King to have things
done as cheap as other men.

5. CIRCUMSPICE

I've always considered Sir Christopher Wren,
As an architect, one of the greatest of men;
And, talking of Epitaphs—much I admire his,
"Circumspice, si Monumentum requiris";
Which an erudite Verger translated to me,
"If you ask for his Monument, Sir-come-spy-see!"

6. A TOAST

Here's to the maiden of bashful fifteen;
  Here's to the widow of fifty;
Here's to the flaunting, extravagant quean;
  And here's to the housewife that's thrifty.
    Let the toast pass,
    Drink to the lass,
I'll warrant she'll prove an excuse for a glass.

7. NOT YET

Men may have rounded Seraglio Point: they have
not yet doubled Cape Turk.

8. INJUNCTION

Be good, sweet maid, and let who can be clever;
  Do noble things, not dream them, all day long;
And so make Life, Death, and that vast For Ever,
  One grand sweet song.

9. UNTUTORED GENIUS

If Shakespeare's genius had been cultivated, those beauties, which we so justly admire in him, would have been undisgraced by those extravagancies, and that nonsense, with which they are so frequently accompanied.

10. COMPROMISE

"A sound Conservative government," said Taper, musingly. "I understand: Tory men and Whig measures."

1. COALS OF FIRE

Heap coals of fire upon his head.

2. PARAMOUR

O thou art fairer than the evening air,
Clad in the beauty of a thousand stars,
Brighter art thou than flaming Jupiter,
When he appeared to hapless Semele,
More lovely than the monarch of the sky
In wanton Arethusa's azured arms,
And none but thou shalt be my paramour.

3. DISILLUSION

The rainbow comes and goes,
And lovely is the rose,
The moon doth with delight
Look round her when the heavens are bare,
Waters on a starry night
Are beautiful and fair:
The sunshine is a glorious birth;
But yet I know, where'er I go,
That there hath passed away a glory from the earth.

4. STYLE

True ease in writing comes from art, not chance,
As those move easiest who have learned to dance.

'Tis not enough no harshness gives offence,
The sound must seem an echo to the sense.

5.   A GOOD INVESTMENT

Mothers of large families, who claim to common sense,
Will find a Tiger well repay the trouble and expense.

6.   FATHER WILLIAM

You are old, Father William, the young man cried,
  And pleasures with youth pass away,
And yet you lament not the days that are gone,
  Now tell me the reason, I pray.

7.   OLD AGE MUST COME

His golden locks time hath to silver turn'd;
  O time too swift, O swiftness never ceasing!
His youth 'gainst time and age hath ever spurned
  But spurn'd in vain; youth waneth by increasing;
Beauty, strength, youth, are flowers but fading seen;
Duty, faith, love, are roots, and ever green.

8.   HANGOVER

I've a head like a concertina, I've a tongue like a
  button-stick,
I've a mouth like an old potato, and I'm more than a
  little sick,

But I've had my fun o' the Corp'ral's Guard; I've
    made the cinders fly.
And I'm here in the Clink for a thundering drink and
    blacking the Corporal's eye.

9. ON WOMEN

Women, then, are only children of a larger growth:
they have an entertaining tattle, and sometimes wit;
but for solid, reasoning good-sense, I never knew in
my life one that had it, or reasoned or acted conse-
quentially for four and twenty hours together.

10. BETTER WAIT

"It is Rooshan; ain't it, Wegg?"

"No, sir. Roman. Roman."

"What's the difference, Wegg?"

"The difference, sir?—There you place me in a
difficulty, Mr. Boffin. Suffice it to observe, that the
difference is best postponed to some other occasion
when Mrs. Boffin does not honour us with her
company."

Group XIII

★

1. CONSIDER THE LILIES

Consider the lilies of the field, how they grow; they toil not, neither do they spin· And yet I say unto you that even Solomon in all his glory was not arrayed like one of these.

2. YOUTH

A boy's will is the wind's will,
And the thoughts of youth are long, long thoughts.

3. ANGLER

Angling may be said to be so like the mathematics, that it can never be fully learnt.

4. EASY MONEY

A young Scotsman of your ability let loose upon the world with £300, what could he not do? It's almost appalling to think of; especially if he went among the English.

5. ONLY A NOVEL

"And what are you reading, Miss—?" "Oh! it is only a novel!" replies the young lady, while she lays down her book with affected indifference, or

39

momentary shame. "It is only Cecilia, or Camilla, or Belinda:" or, in short, only some work in which the most thorough knowledge of human nature, the happiest delineation of its varieties, the liveliest effusions of wit and humour are conveyed to the world in the best chosen language.

6. THE TIGER

Tiger! Tiger! burning bright
In the forests of the night,
What immortal hand or eye
Could frame thy fearful symmetry?

7. A WATERY DEATH

There is a willow grows aslant a brook,
That shows his hoar leaves in the glassy stream;
There with fantastic garlands did she come,
Of crow-flowers, nettles, daisies, and long purples,
That liberal shepherds give a grosser name,
But our cold maids do dead men's fingers call them:
There, on the pendent boughs her coronet weeds
Clambering to hang, an envious sliver broke,
When down her weedy trophies and herself
Fell in the weeping brook. Her clothes spread wide,
And, mermaid-like, awhile they bore her up;
Which time she chanted snatches of old tunes,
As one incapable of her own distress.

8. A POOR LIFE, THE SEA

No man will be a sailor who has contrivance enough to get himself into a jail; for being in a ship is being in a jail, with the chance of being drowned . . . A man in a jail has more room, better food, and commonly better company.

9. CONSERVATISM

Men are conservatives when they are least vigorous, or when they are most luxurious. They are conservatives after dinner.

10. TO BE MISUNDERSTOOD

Is it so bad, then, to be misunderstood? Pythagoras was misunderstood, and Socrates, and Jesus, and Luther, and Copernicus, and Galileo, and Newton, and every pure and wise spirit that ever took flesh. To be great is to be misunderstood.

★

1. FORGIVENESS

Be ye angry, and sin not: let not the sun go down
upon your wrath.

2. ODD

The sun was shining on the sea,
     Shining with all his might;
He did his very best to make
     The billows smooth and bright—
And this was odd, because it was
     The middle of the night.

3. WE LEFT HIM

We carved not a line, and we raised not a stone—
But we left him alone with his glory.

4. FANCY

Tell me where is fancy bred,
     Or in the heart or in the head?
How begot, how nourished?
     Reply, reply.

It is engender'd in the eyes,
With gazing fed; and fancy dies
In the cradle where it lies.
     Let us all ring fancy's bell:
     I'll begin it—Ding, Dong, bell.

5.   TOO HARASSED

Too fast we live, too much are tried,
　　Too harass'd to attain
Wordsworth's sweet calm, or Goethe's wide
　　And luminous view to gain.

6.   A GOOD LIFE

I will make you brooches and toys for your delight
Of bird-song at morning and star-shine at night.
I will make a palace fit for you and me
Of green days in forests and blue days at sea.
I will make my kitchen, and you shall keep your room,
Where white flows the river and bright blows the
　　broom,
And you shall wash your linen and keep your body
In rainfall at morning and dewfall at night.　　[white,

7.   ADIEU

He turned his charger as he spake,
　　Upon the river shore,
He gave his bridle-reins a shake,
　　Said "Adieu for evermore,
　　　　　　My love!
And adieu for evermore."

8.   ONE CHARMER TOO MANY

How happy could I be with either,
　　Were t'other dear charmer away!

But while ye thus tease me together,
　　To neither a word will I say.

9. WHAT'S THE ODDS?

What is the odds so long as the fire of soul is kindled at the taper of conviviality, and the wing of friendship never moults a feather!

10. SALAMIS

A king sate on the rocky brow
　　Which looks o'er sea-born Salamis;
And ships, by thousands, lay below,
　　And men in nations;—all were his!
He counted them at break of day—
And when the sun set where were they?

1. BUT ONE LAW

There is but one law for all, namely, that law which governs all law, the law of our Creator, the law of humanity, justice, equity—the law of nature, and of nations.

2. THE KINGDOM

But (when so sad thou canst not sadder)
    Cry:—and upon thy so sore loss
Shall shine the traffic of Jacob's ladder
    Pitched betwixt Heaven and Charing Cross.

3. IMMORTALITY

It must be so—Plato, thou reason'st well!—
Else whence this pleasing hope, this fond desire,
This longing after immortality?
Or whence this secret dread, and inward horror,
Of falling into naught? Why shrinks the soul
Back on herself, and startles at destruction?
'Tis the divinity that stirs within us;
'Tis heaven itself, that points out an hereafter,
And intimates eternity to man.

4. KNOWLEDGE

The knowledge of man is as the waters, some descending from above, and some springing from beneath; the one informed by the light of nature, the other inspired by divine revelation.

5. I SHALL REMEMBER

I shall remember while the light lives yet
And in the night time I shall not forget.

6. DISILLUSIONED

It goes so heavily with my disposition that this goodly frame, the earth, seems to me a sterile promontory; this most excellent canopy, the air, look you, this brave o'erhanging firmament, this majestical roof fretted with golden fire, why, it appears no other thing to me but a foul and pestilent congregation of vapours. What a piece of work is a man! How noble in reason! how infinite in faculty! in form, in moving, how express and admirable! in action, how like an angel! in apprehension how like a god! the beauty of the world! the paragon of animals! And yet, to me, what is this quintessence of dust? man delights not me; no, nor woman neither, though, by your smiling, you seem to say so.

7. INSPIRATION

It was at Rome, on the 15th of October 1764, as I sat musing amidst the ruins of the Capitol, while the barefooted friars were singing vespers in the Temple of Jupiter, that the idea of writing the decline and fall of the city first started to my mind.

8. WHO WILL REMEMBER?

Here lies a most beautiful lady,
  Light of step and heart was she;
I think she was the most beautiful lady
  That ever was in the West Country.
But beauty vanishes; beauty passes;
  However rare—rare it be;
And when I crumble, who will remember
  This lady of the West Country?

9. THE PEOPLE

If by the people you understand the multitude, the *hoi polloi*, 'tis no matter what they think; they are sometimes in the right, sometimes in the wrong; their judgment is a mere lottery.

10. COME, BUY AND EAT

Ho, every one that thirsteth, come ye to the waters, and he that hath no money; come ye, buy and eat; yea, come, buy wine and milk without money and without price.

Wherefore do ye spend money for that which is not bread? and your labour for that which satisfieth not?

★

1. AWAKE

Now it is high time to awake out of sleep: for now
is our salvation nearer than when we believed.

2. PIS ALLER

Sweetest love, I do not go,
For weariness of thee,
Nor in hope the world can show
A fitter Love for me;
But since that I
Must die at last, 'tis best,
To use my self in jest
Thus by fain'd deaths to die.

3. LAUGH

Laugh, and the world laughs with you;
Weep, and you weep alone;
For the sad old earth must borrow its mirth,
But has trouble enough of its own.

4. DEATH

Ay, but to die, and go we know not where;
To lie in cold obstruction and to rot;
This sensible warm motion to become
A kneaded clod; and the delighted spirit

To bathe in fiery floods, or to reside
In thrilling region of thick-ribbèd ice;
To be imprisoned in the viewless winds,
And blown with restless violence round about
The pendent world!

5. WHY NOT?

It ought to be quite as natural and straight-forward a matter for a labourer to take his pension from his parish, because he has deserved well of his parish, as for a man in higher rank to take his pension from his country, because he has deserved well of his country.

6. THE AESTHETE

Then a sentimental passion of a vegetable fashion must
  excite your languid spleen,
An attachment à la Plato, for a bashful young potato,
  or a not too French French bean!
Though the Philistines may jostle, you will rank as an
  apostle in the high aesthetic band,
If you walk down Piccadilly with a poppy or a lily
  in your medieval hand.
  And everyone will say,
  As you walk your flowery way,
"If he's content with a vegetable love which would
  certainly not suit *me*,
Why, what a most particularly pure young man this
  pure young man must be!"

7. BALLAD

The farmer's daughter hath soft brown hair;
  (Butter and eggs and a pound of cheese)
And I met with a ballad, I can't say where,
  Which wholly consisted of lines like these.

8. A PROFOUND TRUTH

It costs a lot of money to die comfortably.

9. WHITE HORSES

Now the great winds shoreward blow;
Now the salt tides seaward flow;
Now the wild white horses play,
Champ and chafe and toss in the spray.

10. WATCHMAN

Watchman, what of the night? Watchman, what of
  the night?
The watchman said, The morning cometh, and also
  the night.

★

1. ENCONIUM

He was a verray parfit gentil knight.

2. HERITAGE

In our halls is hung
Armoury of the invincible Knights of old:
We must be free or die, who speak the tongue
That Shakespeare spake: the faith and morals hold
Which Milton held. In everything we are sprung
Of Earth's first blood, have titles manifold.

3. SUBTLETY

The merchant, to secure his treasure,
Conveys it in a borrowed name:
Euphelia serves to grace my measure;
But Chloe is my real flame.

4. RISE AND DECLINE

In the youth of a state arms do flourish; in the
middle age of a state, learning; and then both of
them together for a time; in the declining age of a
state, mechanical arts and merchandise.

5. LUNA

That orbèd maiden, with white fire laden,
    Whom mortals call the moon,
Glides glimmering o'er my fleece-like floor,
    By the midnight breezes strewn;
And wherever the beat of her unseen feet,
    Which only the angels hear,
May have broken the woof of my tent's thin roof,
    The stars peep behind her and peer;

6. RECOLLECTION

I have been here before,
    But when or how I cannot tell;
I know the grass beyond the door,
    The sweet keen smell,
The sighing sound, the lights around the shore.

7. IF YOU WOULD KNOW . .

If you would know the value of money, go and try
to borrow some; for he that goes a borrowing goes a
sorrowing.

8. SOMETIMES . . .

Sometimes we see a cloud that's dragonish;
A vapour sometime like a bear or lion,
A tower'd citadel, a pendant rock,
A forked mountain, or blue promontory
With trees upon't, that nod unto the world

And mock our eyes with air: thou has seen these signs;
They are black vesper's pageants.

9. TIME FOR TEA

Now stir the fire, and close the shutters fast,
Let fall the curtains, wheel the sofa round,
And, while the bubbling and loud-hissing urn
Throws up a steamy column, and the cups,
That cheer but not inebriate, wait on each,
So let us welcome peaceful ev'ning in.

10. ALL'S OVER

Since there's no help, come let us kiss and part,
Nay, I have done: you get no more of me,
And I am glad, yea glad with all my heart,
That thus so cleanly, I myself can free,
Shake hands for ever, cancel all our vows,
And when we meet at any time again,
Be it not seen in either of our brows,
That we one jot of former love retain;

1. FAITH

For in him we live, and move, and have our being.

2. NOT THE PALM WITHOUT THE DUST

I cannot praise a fugitive and cloistered virtue,
unexercised and unbreathed, that never sallies out
and sees her adversary, but slinks out of the race,
where that immortal garland is to be run for, not
without dust and heat.

3. ENOUGH

The earth, that is sufficient.
I do not want the constellations any nearer,
I know they are very well where they are,
I know they suffice for those who belong to them.

4. A MIND DISEASED

Canst thou not minister to a mind diseas'd,
Pluck from the memory a rooted sorrow,
Raze out the written troubles of the brain,
And with some sweet oblivious antidote
Cleanse the stuff'd bosom of that perilous stuff
Which weighs upon the heart?

5. A VIRGIN HEART

How sweet are looks that ladies bend
　　On whom their favours fall!
For them I battle till the end
　　To save from shame and thrall;
But all my heart is drawn above,
　　My knees are bow'd in crypt and shrine:
I never felt the kiss of love
　　Nor maiden's hand in mine.
More bounteous aspects on me beam,
　　Me mightier transports move and thrill;
So keep I fair thro' faith and prayer
　　A virgin heart in work and will.

6. BEFORE BATTLE

Now all the youth of England are on fire,
And silken dalliance in the wardrobe lies;
Now thrive the armourers, and honour's thought
Reigns solely in the breast of every man:
They sell the pasture now to buy the horse,
Following the mirror of all Christian kings,
With wingèd heels, as English Mercuries.

7. TOIL

For men must work, and women must weep,
And there's little to earn, and many to keep,
Though the harbour bar be moaning.

8. EPITAPH

Here lies our good Edmund, whose genius was such,
We scarcely can praise it, or blame it too much;
Who, born for the Universe, narrow'd his mind,
And to party gave up what was meant for mankind.
Though fraught with all learning, yet straining his
    throat
To persuade Tommy Townshend to lend him a vote;
Who, too deep for his hearers, still went on refining.
And thought of convincing, while they thought of
    dining;
Though equal to all things, for all things unfit,
Too nice for a statesman, too proud for a wit.

9. NOT DIFFICULT

Any man may be in good spirits and good temper
when he's well dressed. There an't much credit in
that.

10. THE POINT OF VIEW

What makes all doctrines plain and clear?
About two hundred pounds a year.
And that which was prov'd true before,
Prove false again? Two hundred more.

1. AFTER MANY DAYS

Cast thy bread upon the waters: for thou shalt find
it after many days.

2. THE THOUGHT OF THEE

I must not think of thee; and, tired yet strong,
I shun the thought that lurks in all delight—
The thought of thee—and in the blue heaven's height,
And in the sweetest passage of a song.

3. IMMORTALITY

Our birth is but a sleep and a forgetting:
   The Soul that rises with us, our life's Star,
Hath had elsewhere its setting,
   And cometh from afar:
Not in entire forgetfulness,
And not in utter nakedness,
But trailing clouds of glory do we come
   From God, who is our home:
Heaven lies about us in our infancy!

4. A MATTER FOR REJOICING

I rejoice that America has resisted. Three millions
of people, so dead to all the feelings of liberty, as

voluntarily to submit to be slaves, would have been fit instruments to make slaves of the rest.

5. SUSSEX

If I ever become a rich man,
  Or if ever I grow to be old,
I will build a house with deep thatch
  To shelter me from the cold,
And there shall the Sussex songs be sung
  And the story of Sussex told.

6. A DEAD POET

He has out-soared the shadow of our night;
Envy and calumny and hate and pain,
And that unrest which men miscall delight,
Can touch him not and torture not again;
From the contagion of the world's slow stain
He is secure, and now can never mourn
A heart grown cold, a head grown grey in vain.

7. IVY FOR ME

Oh roses for the flush of youth,
  And laurel for the perfect prime;
But pluck an ivy branch for me
  Grown old before my time.

8. OXFORD

Noon strikes on England, noon on Oxford town,
Beauty she was statue cold—there's blood upon her
  gown:
Noon of my dreams, O noon!
Proud and godly kings had built her, long ago,
With her towers and tombs and statues all arow,
With her fair and floral air and the love that lingers
  there,
And the streets where the great men go.

9. ADORATION

When he shall die,
Take him and cut him out in little stars,
And he will make the face of heaven so fine
That all the world will be in love with night,
And pay no worship to the garish sun.

10. CONNOISSEUR

"I rather like bad wine," said Mr. Mountchesney;
"one gets so bored with good wine."

1. PRODIGAL'S RETURN

Bring hither the fatted calf and kill it.

2. BLACKSMITH

Under a spreading chestnut tree
 The village smithy stands;
The smith, a mighty man is he,
 With large and sinewy hands;
And the muscles of his brawny arms
 As strong as iron bands.

3. VICTORY

"What a glorious thing must be a victory, Sir."
"The greatest tragedy in the world, Madam, except a
defeat."

4. TRAPPED

The Devil, having nothing else to do,
Went off to tempt my Lady Poltigrue.
My Lady, tempted by a private whim,
To his extreme annoyance, tempted him.

5. A PARADOX

In civil business; what first? boldness; what second
and third ? boldness: and yet boldness is a child of
ignorance and baseness.

6. JOY

"I have no name:
I am but two days old."
What shall I call thee?
"I happy am,
Joy is my name."
Sweet joy befall thee!

7. HAPPY IS ENGLAND

Happy is England! I could be content
To see no other verdure than its own;
To feel no other breezes than are blown
Through its tall woods with high romances blent.

8. PARADISE

Here with a Loaf of Bread beneath the bough,
A Flask of Wine, a Book of Verse—and Thou
    Beside me singing in the Wilderness—
And Wilderness is Paradise enow.

9. THE CURSE

An orphan's curse would drag to hell
A spirit from on high;
But oh! more horrible than that
Is the curse in a dead man's eye.

He was in logic a great critic,
Profoundly skill'd in analytic.
He could distinguish, and divide
A hair 'twixt south and south-west side.
On either which he would dispute
Confute, change hands, and still confute.

1. THE JOURNEY

Does the road wind up-hill all the way?
   Yes, to the very end.
Will the day's journey take the whole long day?
   From morn to night, my friend.

2. BEN ADHEM'S VISION

Abou Ben Adhem (may his tribe increase!)
Awoke one night from a deep dream of peace,
And saw, within the moonlight in his room,
Making it rich, and like a lily in bloom,
An angel writing in a book of gold.

3. IN MANY WAYS . . .

The old order changeth, yielding place to new,
And God fulfils himself in many ways,
Lest one good custom should corrupt the world.

4. IN REMEMBRANCE

Bring the rathe primrose that forsaken dies,
  The tufted crow-toe, and pale jessamine,
The white pink, and the pansy freakt with jet,
  The glowing violet,
The musk-rose, and the well-attir'd woodbine,
With cowslips wan that hang the pensive head,

And every flower that sad embroidery wears.
Bid amaranthus all his beauty shed,
And daffodillies fill their cups with tears,
To strew the laureate hearse.

5. EFFORT

To travel hopefully is a better thing than to arrive,
and the true success is to labour.

6. SOME SAY . . .

It faded on the crowing of the cock.
Some say that ever 'gainst that season comes
Wherein our Saviour's birth is celebrated,
The bird of dawning singeth all night long;
And then, they say, no spirit can walk abroad;
The nights are wholesome; then no planets strike,
No fairy takes, nor witch hath power to charm,
So hallow'd and so gracious is the time.

7. THE CUCKOO

When daisies pied and violets blue
    And lady-smocks all silver-white
And cuckoo-buds of yellow hue
    Do paint the meadows with delight,
The cuckoo then, on every tree,
Mocks married men; for thus sings he,
            Cuckoo;
Cuckoo, cuckoo; O, word of fear,
Unpleasing to a married ear!

8. CARPE DIEM

One Moment in Annihilation's Waste,
One Moment of the Well of Life to taste—
    The Stars are Setting and the Caravan
Starts for the Dawn of Nothing—Oh, make haste!

9. A SAVAGE PLACE

But oh! that deep romantic chasm which slanted
Down the green hill athwart a cedarn cover!
A savage place! as holy and enchanted
As e'er beneath a waning moon was haunted
By woman wailing for her demon-lover!

10. ONE LEAK

One leak will sink a ship, and one sin will destroy
a sinner.

1. THE PILOT

Last came and last did go,
The Pilot of the Galilean lake,
Two massy keys he bore of metals twain,
The golden opes, the iron shuts amain.

2. DUSK

The lamps are going out all over Europe; we shall
not see them lit again in our lifetime.

3. THE INFINITE

Our noisy years seem moments in the being
Of the eternal Silence: truths that wake,
    To perish never:
Which neither listlessness, nor mad endeavour,
    Nor Man nor Boy,
Nor all that is at enmity with joy,
Can utterly abolish or destroy!

4. CONFIDENCE

He either fears his fate too much,
    Or his deserts are small,
That puts it not unto the touch,
    To win or lose it all.

5.   LAUGHTER

I live in a constant endeavour to fence against the infirmities of ill health, and other evils of life, by mirth; being firmly persuaded that every time a man smiles, but much more so, when he laughs, that it adds something to this Fragment of Life.

6.   RENUNCIATION

I'll give my jewels for a set of beads,
My gorgeous palace for a hermitage,
My gay apparel for an almsman's gown,
My figur'd goblets for a dish of wood,
My sceptre for a palmer's walking staff,
My subjects for a pair of carved saints,
And my large kingdom for a little grave.

7.   TO DAFFODILS

Fair daffodils, we weep to see
You haste away so soon:
As yet the early-rising sun
Has not attain'd his noon.
    Stay, stay,
Until the hasting day
    Has run
But to the even-song;
And, having pray'd together, we
Will go with you along.

8. THE JURY

"Write that down," the King said to the jury, and the jury eagerly wrote down all three dates on their slates, and then added them up, and reduced the answer to shillings and pence.

9. O LYRIC LOVE

O lyric Love, half angel and half bird
And all a wonder and a wild desire.

10. AND SHALL TRELAWNY DIE?

A good sword and a trusty hand!
   A merry heart and true!
King James's men shall understand
   What Cornish lads can do.

And have they fix'd the where and when?
   And shall Trelawny die?
Here's twenty thousand Cornish men
   Will know the reason why!

★

1. FILL THE CUP

Ah, fill the Cup—what boots it to repeat
How Time is slipping underneath our Feet:
    Unborn TOMORROW, and dead YESTERDAY,
Why fret about them if TODAY be sweet!

2. WHERE IS IT NOW?

Whither is fled the visionary gleam?
Where is it now, the glory and the dream?

3. ATHENS

Athens, the eye of Greece, mother of arts
And eloquence, native to famous wits
Or hospitable, in her sweet recess,
City or suburb, studious walks and shades;
See there the olive grove of Academe,
Plato's retirement, where the Attic bird
Trills her thick-warbled notes the summer long.

4. REGRETS

And the stately ships go on
    To their haven under the hill;
But O for the touch of a vanish'd hand,
    And the sound of a voice that is still!

5. TO THE MOON

With how sad steps, O Moon, thou climb'st the skies!
How silently, and with how wan a face!
What! may it be that even in heavenly place
That busy archer his sharp arrows tries?

6. PORTENTS

When beggars die, there are no comets seen;
The heavens themselves blaze forth the death of
   princes.

7. THE GRAND PANJANDRUM

So she went into the garden to cut a cabbage-leaf,
to make an apple-pie; and at the same time a great
she-bear, coming up the street, pops its head into the
shop. "What! no soap?" So he died, and she very
imprudently married the barber; and there were
present the Picninnies, and the Joblillies, and the
Garyalies, and the grand Panjandrum himself, with
the little round button at top, and they all fell to
playing the game of catch as catch can, till the gun
powder ran out at the heels of their boots.

8. REFLECTION

Upwards of five-hundred-thousand two-legged
animals without feathers lie around us, in horizontal
positions; their heads all in nightcaps, and full of the
foolishest dreams.

9.   MYSTERY

A good parson once said, that where mystery begins, religion ends. Cannot I say, as truly at least, of human laws, that where mystery begins, justice ends?

10.   OPPORTUNITY

There is a tide in the affairs of men,
Which, taken at the flood, leads on to fortune;
Omitted, all the voyage of their life
Is bound in shallows and in miseries.
On such a full sea are we now afloat,
And we must take the current when it serves,
Or lose our ventures.

★

1. ONE THING IS CERTAIN

For we brought nothing into this world, and it is
certain we can carry nothing out.

2. HE WAS THERE

"Tell them I came, and no one answered,
"That I kept my word," he said.

3. HAPPY WARRIOR

Who is the happy Warrior? Who is he
That every man in arms should wish to be?
It is the generous spirit, who, when brought
Among the tasks of real life, hath wrought
Upon the plan that pleased his childish thought:
Whose high endeavours are an inward light
That makes the path before him always bright:
Who, with a natural instinct to discern
What knowledge can perform, is diligent to learn.

4. NIGHTFALL

Now came still evening on, and twilight gray
Had in her sober livery all things clad;
Silence accompanied, for beast and bird,
They to their grassy couch, these to their nests,

Were slunk, all but the wakeful nightingale;
She all night long her amorous descant sung;

5.   THE SEA

I will go back to the great sweet mother,
Mother and lover of men, the sea.
I will go down to her, I and no other,
Close with her, kiss her and mix her with me.

6.   THE MAKING OF MAN

Before the beginning of years
    There came to the making of man
Time with a gift of tears,
    Grief with a glass that ran.
Pleasure with pain for leaven,
    Summer with flowers that fell,
Remembrance fallen from heaven,
    And Madness risen from hell,
Strength without hands to smite,
    Love that endures for a breath;
Night, the shadow of light,
    And Life, the shadow of death.

7.   THE QUEEN

The barge she sat in, like a burnish'd throne,
Burn'd on the water; the poop was beaten gold,
Purple the sails, and so perfumed, that
The winds were love-sick with them, the oars were
    silver,

Which to the tune of flutes kept stroke, and made
The water which they beat to follow faster,
As amorous of their strokes.

8. FIASCO

I left the room with silent dignity, but caught my
foot in the mat.

9. SALLY

Of all the girls that are so smart
There's none like pretty Sally,
She is the darling of my heart,
And she lives in our alley.

10. DYING GLADIATOR

He heard it, but he heeded not—his eyes
Were with his heart, and that was far away;
He reck'd not of the life he lost nor prize,
But where his rude hut by the Danube lay,
There were his young barbarians all at play,
There was their Dacian mother—he, their sire,
Butcher'd to make a Roman holiday.

Group XXV

★

1. WISDOM

Wisdom is the principal thing; therefore get wisdom; and with all thy getting get understanding.

2. RAINBOW

My heart leaps up when I behold
   A rainbow in the sky:
So was it when my life began;
So is it now I am a man:
So be it when I shall grow old,
   Or let me die!
The Child is father of the Man;
And I could wish my days to be
Bound each to each by natural piety.

3. A GREAT MAN

Foremost captain of his time,
Rich in saving common-sense,
And, as the greatest only are,
In his simplicity sublime.
O good grey head which all men knew!

4. ORACLES

As who should say, "I am Sir Oracle,
And when I ope my lips let no dog bark!"

O, my Antonio, I do know of these,
That therefore only are reputed wise,
For saying nothing.

5. AS DREAMS ARE MADE ON

Or revels now are ended. These our actors
As I foretold you, were all spirits and
Are melted into air, into thin air:
And, like the baseless fabric of this vision,
The cloud-capped towers, the gorgeous palaces,
The solemn temples, the great globe itself,
Yea, all which it inherit, shall dissolve
And, like this insubstantial pageant faded,
Leave not a rack behind. We are such stuff
As dreams are made on, and our little life
Is rounded with a sleep.

6. THEY LITTLE KNOW

Strange to say what delight we married people have
to see these poor fools decoyed into our condition.

7. COLOSSUS

His legs bestrid the ocean; his rear'd arm
Crested the world; his voice was propertied
As all the tunèd spheres, and that to friends;
But when he meant to quail and shake the orb,
He was as rattling thunder. For his bounty,
There was no winter in't; an autumn was

That grew the more by reaping; his delights
Were dolphin-like, they show'd his back above
The elements they liv'd in; in his livery
Walk'd crowns and crownets, realms and islands were
As plates dropp'd from his pocket.

8.   A FULL LIFE

I strove with none; for none was worth my strife;
   Nature I loved, and next to Nature, Art;
I warmed both hands before the fire of life;
   It sinks, and I am ready to depart.

9.   ONE GOOD DEED

  It is a far, far better thing that I do, than I have ever
done; it is a far, far better rest that I go to, than I have
ever known.

10.   APRIL

Oh, to be in England
   Now that April's there,
And whoever wakes in England
   Sees, some morning, unaware,
That the lowest boughs and the brushwood sheaf
   Round the elm-tree bole are in tiny leaf,
While the chaffinch sings on the orchard bough
   In England—now!

1. TILL DEATH US DO PART

Intreat me not to leave thee, or to return from following after thee: for whither thou goest, I will go; and where thou lodgest I will lodge; thy people shall be my people, and thy God, my God. Where thou diest, will I die, and there will I be buried; the Lord do so to me, and more also, if ought but death part thee and me.

2. SHE IS COMING

There has fallen a splendid tear
  From the passion-flower at the gate.
She is coming, my dove, my dear;
  She is coming, my life, my fate;
The red rose cries, "She is near, she is near;"
  And the white rose weeps, "She is late;"
The larkspur listens, "I hear, I hear;"
  And the lily whispers, "I wait."

3. DISILLUSION

To-morrow, and to-morrow, and to-morrow,
Creeps in this petty pace from day to day,
To the last syllable of recorded time;
And all our yesterdays have lighted fools
The way to dusty death. Out, out, brief candle!

Life's but a walking shadow, a poor player,
That struts and frets his hour upon the stage,
And then is heard no more; it is a tale
Told by an idiot full of sound and fury,
Signifying nothing.

4. DIVERSITY

It is the common wonder of all men, how among
so many millions of faces, there should be none alike.

5. THE SPUR

Alas! what boots it with uncessant care
To tend the homely, slighted, shepherd's trade,
And strictly meditate the thankless Muse?
Were it not better done, as others use,
To sport with Amaryllis in the shade,
Or with the tangles of Neaera's hair?
Fame is the spur that the clear spirit doth raise
(That last infirmity of noble mind)
To scorn delights, and live laborious days.

6. SARAH

"A clear fire, a clean hearth, and the rigour of the
game." This was the celebrated wish of old Sarah
Battle (now with God), who, next to her devotions,
loved a good game of whist.

7. LOVE IN PRISON

When Love with unconfinèd wings
    Hovers within my gates,
And my divine Althea brings
    To whisper at the grates;
When I lie tangled in her hair,
    And fettered to her eye;
The Gods, that wanton in the air,
    Know no such liberty.

8. IT WOULDN'T DO

Said John—It is my wedding-day,
    And all the world would stare,
If wife should dine at Edmonton
    And I should dine at Ware.

9. SUNRISE

Round the Cape of a sudden came the sea,
And the sun looked over the mountain's rim;
And straight was a path of gold for him,
And the need of a world of men for me.

10. A GRAND SOUND

There's a bell in Moscow,
    While on tower and kiosk O
In Saint Sophia
      The Turkman gets,

And loud in air
Calls men to prayer
From the tapering summits
    Of tall minarets.
Such empty phantom
I freely grant them;
But there's an anthem
    More dear to me—
'Tis the bells of Shandon
That sound so grand on
The pleasant waters
    Of the River Lee.

1. DESTINY

The stars in their courses fought against Sisera.

2. THESE WERE LOVELY

But the loveliest things of beauty God ever has
    showed to me,
Are her voice, and her hair, and eyes, and the dear
    red curve of her lips.

3. "PEOPLE MATTER"

The worth of a State, in the long run, is the worth
of the individuals composing it.

4. PRELUDE TO MURDER

Now o'er the one half-world
Nature seems dead, and wicked dreams abuse
The curtain'd sleep; witchcraft celebrates
Pale Hecate's offerings; and wither'd murder,
Alarum'd by his sentinel, the wolf,
Whose howl's his watch, thus with his stealthy pace,
With Tarquin's ravishing strides, towards his design
Moves like a ghost. Thou sure and firm-set earth,
Hear not my steps, which way they walk, for fear
The very stones prate of my whereabout,
And take the present horror from the time
Which now suits with it.

5. FOR EVER ENGLAND

If I should die, think only this of me:
That there's some corner of a foreign field
That is for ever England.

6. GET THEE HENCE

Hence, loathed Melancholy,
  Of Cerebus, and blackest Midnight born,
In Stygian cave forlorn,
  'Mongst horrid shapes, and shrieks, and sights
  unholy.

7. CANADA ASSERTS HERSELF

A Nation spoke to a Nation,
A Throne sent word to a Throne;
"Daughter am I in my mother's house,
But mistress in my own.
The gates are mine to open,
As the gates are mine to close,
And I abide by my Mother's House."
Said our Lady of the Snows.

8. THE ROMANS

Then none was for a party;
  Then all were for the state;
Then the great man helped the poor,
  And the poor man loved the great:
Then lands were fairly portioned;

Then spoils were fairly sold:
The Romans were like brothers
In the brave days of old.

9. WHEN WE ARE MARRIED

Don't let us be familiar or fond, nor kiss before folks, like my Lady Fadler and Sir Francis; No go to Hyde-Park together the first Sunday in a new chariot, to provoke eyes and whispers, and then never be seen there together again; as if we were proud of one another the first week, and asham'd of one another ever after . . . Let us be very strange and well-bred: Let us be as strange as if we had been married a great while, and as well-bred as if we were not married at all.

10. A GOOD LIFE

One who never turned his back but marched breast
    forward,
  Never doubted clouds would break,
Never dreamed, though right were worsted, wrong
    would triumph,
  Held we fall to rise, are baffled to fight better,
  Sleep to wake.

Group XXVIII

★

1. TO-MORROW . . .

Let us eat and drink, for to-morrow we shall die.

2. WHEN YOU ARE OLD

When you are old and gray and full of sleep,
And nodding by the fire, take down this book,
And slowly read, and dream of the soft look
Your eyes had once, and of their shadows deep;
How many loved your moments of glad grace,
And loved your beauty with love false or true,
But one man loved the pilgrim soul in you,
And loved the sorrows of your changing face;
And bending down beside the glowing bars,
Murmurs, a little sadly, how Love fled
And paced upon the mountains overhead
And hid his face amid a crowd of stars.

3. I FOUND HIM

I found Him in the shining of the stars,
I mark'd Him in the flowering of His fields,
But in His ways with men, I find Him not.

4. ASK YOURSELF

Does the Eagle know what is in the pit
    Or wilt thou go ask the Mole?

Can Wisdom be put in a silver rod,
  Or Love in a golden bowl?

5. LOVE

And the night has a thousand eyes,
    And the day but one;
  Yet the light of the bright world dies,
    With the dying sun.

The mind has a thousand eyes,
    And the heart but one;
  Yet the light of a whole life dies,
    When love is done.

6. THE PATRIOT

Breathes there the man, with soul so dead,
Who never to himself hath said,
  This is my own, my native land!
Whose heart hath ne'er within him burn'd,
As home his footsteps he hath turn'd
  From wandering on a foreign strand!

7. THE JUMBLIES

Far and few, far and few,
  Are the lands where the Jumblies live;
Their heads are green, and their hands are blue,
  And they went to sea in a Sieve.

8. FOLLY

When lovely woman stoops to folly
    And finds too late that men betray,
What charm can soothe her melancholy,
    What art can wash her guilt away?

9. BLUNDER

He had forty-two boxes, all carefully packed,
    With his name painted clearly on each:
But, since he omitted to mention the fact,
    They were all left behind on the beach.

10. SIC TRANSIT . . .

Farewell! a long farewell, to all my greatness!
This is the state of man: to-day he puts forth
The tender leaves of hope; To-morrow blossoms,
And bears his blushing honours thick upon him;
The third day comes a frost, a killing frost;
And, when he thinks, good easy man, full surely
His greatness is a-ripening, nips his root,
And then he falls, as I do. I have ventur'd
Like little wanton boys that swim on bladders,
This many summers in a sea of glory,
But far beyond my depth: my high-blown pride
At length broke under me, and now has left me
Weary and old with service, to the mercy
Of a rude stream that must for ever hide me.

★

1.   LOVELINESS

I am the rose of Sharon, and the lily of the valleys.

2.   LONDON

Earth has not anything to show more fair;
Dull would he be of soul who could pass by
A sight so touching in its majesty:
This City now doth, like a garment wear
The beauty of the morning: silent, bare,
Ships, towers, domes, theatres, and temples lie
Open unto the fields, and to the sky;
All bright and glittering in the smokeless air.

3.   I FLED HIM

I fled Him, down the nights and down the days;
  I fled Him, down the arches of the years;
I fled Him, down the labyrinthine ways
  Of my own mind; and in the mist of tears
I hid from Him, and under running laughter.

4.   A SUMMER NIGHT

How sweet the moonlight sleeps upon this bank!
Here we will sit, and let the sounds of music
Creep in our ears: soft stillness and the night
Become the touches of sweet harmony.

5. HISTORY

I have read somewhere or other—in Dionysius of Halicarnassus, I think—that History is Philosophy teaching by examples.

6. THE PILGRIM

Give me my scallop-shell of quiet,
   My staff of faith to walk upon,
My scrip of joy, immortal diet,
   My bottle of salvation,
My gown of glory, hope's true gage,
And thus I'll take my pilgrimage.

7. THE INFIDEL

I do not know, Sir, that the fellow is an infidel; but if he be an infidel, he is an infidel as a dog is an infidel; that is to say, he has never thought upon the subject.

8. TRUE AND FALSE WEALTH

Ill fares the land, to hast'ning ills a prey,
Where wealth accumulates, and men decay;
Princes and lords may flourish, or may fade;
A breath can make them, as a breath has made;
But a bold peasantry, their country's pride,
When once destroy'd, can never be supplied.

"I'm very brave generally," he went on in a low voice: "only to-day I happen to have a headache."

10.   THE PATHLESS WOODS

There is a pleasure in the pathless woods,
There is a rapture in the lonely shore,
There is society, where none intrudes,
By the deep sea, and music in its roar:
I love not man the less, but Nature more,
From these our interviews, in which I steal
From all I may be, or have been before,
To mingle with the Universe, and feel
What I can ne'er express, yet cannot all conceal.

1. CONVICTION

For I am persuaded, that neither death, nor life, nor angels, nor principalities, nor powers, nor things present, nor things to come, nor height, nor depth, nor any other creature, shall be able to separate us from the love of God.

2. I REMEMBER

I remember, I remember,
  The house where I was born,
The little window where the sun
  Came peeping in at morn;
He never came a wink too soon,
  Nor brought too long a day,
But now, I often wish the night
  Had borne my breath away!

3. POET IN LOVE

I know the way she went
Home with her maiden posy,
For her feet have touch'd the meadows
And left the daisies rosy.

4. TRUTH

What is truth? said jesting Pilate; and would not stay for an answer.

5. GENTLENESS

The gentle mind by gentle deeds is known.
For a man by nothing is so well bewray'd,
As by his manners.

6. THE NEW ORDER

The oracles are dumb,
No voice or hideous hum
Runs through the arched roof in words deceiving.
Apollo from his shrine
Can no more divine,
With hollow shriek the steep of Delphos leaving.
No nightly trance or breathèd spell,
Inspires the pale-eyed priest from the prophetic cell.

7. BEWITCHED

I met a lady in the meads
Full beautiful, a faery's child;
Her hair was long, her foot was light,
And her eyes were wild.

I set her on my pacing steed,
And nothing else saw all day long;
For sideways would she lean, and sing
A faery's song.

8. FOR THE ROYAL NAVY

Ye Mariners of England
   That guard our native seas,
Whose flag has braved, a thousand years,
   The battle and the breeze—
Your glorious standard launch again
   To match another foe !
And sweep through the deep,
   While the stormy winds do blow—
While the battle rages loud and long,
   And the stormy winds do blow.

9. THREE POETS

Three poets, in three distant ages born,
Greece, Italy and England did adorn.
The first in loftiness of thought surpass'd ;
The next in majesty, in both the last :
The force of nature could no farther go ;
To make a third she join'd the former two.

10. BONNIE LESLEY

O saw ye bonnie Lesley
   As she gaed o'er the border ?
She's gane, like Alexander,
   To spread her conquests farther.

★

1. ENGLAND

What have I done for you,
    England, my England?
What is there I would not do,
    England, my own?

2. NATURE

    I have learned
To look on nature, not as in the hour
Of thoughtless youth; but hearing often-times
The still, sad music of humanity,
Nor harsh nor grating, though of ample power
To chasten or subdue. And I have felt
A presence that disturbs me with the joy
Of elevated thoughts; a sense sublime
Of something far more deeply interfused,
Whose dwelling is the light of setting suns,
And the round ocean and the living air,
And the blue sky, and in the mind of man.

3. IT MAY BE . . .

    Come, my friends,
'Tis not too late to seek a newer world.
Push off, and sitting well in order smite
The sounding furrows; for my purpose holds
To sail beyond the sunset, and the baths

Of all the western stars, until I die.
It may be that the gulfs will wash us down:
It may be we shall touch the Happy Isles,
And see the great Achilles, whom we knew.
Tho' much is taken, much abides; and tho'
We are not now that strength which in old days
Moved earth and heaven; that which we are, we are;
One equal temper of heroic hearts,
Made weak by time and fate, but strong in will
To strive, to seek, to find, and not to yield.

4.   SILVIA

Who is Silvia? what is she,
　　That all our swains commend her?
Holy, fair, and wise is she;
　　The heaven such grace did lend her,
That she might admired be.

5.   SPIRIT OF NIGHT

Swiftly walk over the western wave,
　　Spirit of Night!
Out of the misty eastern cave,
Where, all the long and lone daylight,
Thou wovest dreams of joy and fear,
Which make thee terrible and dear,—
　　Swift be thy flight!

6. A PROPHECY

Methinks I see in my mind a noble and puissant nation rousing herself like a strong man after sleep, and shaking her invincible locks. Methinks I see her as an eagle mewing her mighty youth, and kindling her undazzled eyes at the full mid-day beam.

7. A GARDEN

I have a garden of my own,
But so with roses overgrown,
And lilies, that you would it guess
To be a little wilderness.

8. SLEEP

Oh Sleep! it is a gentle thing,
 Beloved from pole to pole!
To Mary Queen the praise be given!
She sent the gentle sleep from Heaven,
 That slid into my soul.

9. MIND AND MATTER

"Mind and matter," said the lady in the wig, "glide swift into the vortex of immensity. Howls the sublime, and softly sleeps the calm Ideal, in the whispering chambers of Imagination."

That low man seeks a little thing to do,
  Sees it and does it:
This high man, with a great thing to pursue,
  Dies ere he knows it.
That low man goes on adding one to one,
  His hundred's soon hit:
This high man, aiming at a million,
  Misses an unit.

★

1. SACRIFICE

Greater love hath no man than this, that a man lay down his life for his friends.

2. THE PEOPLE

You can fool all the people some of the time, and some of the people all the time, but you can not fool all the people all the time.

3. CARRION CROW

Old Adam, the carrion crow,
    The old crow of Cairo;
He sat in the shower, and let it flow
    Under his tail and over his crest;
        And through every feather
        Leak'd the wet weather;
And the bough swung under his nest;
For his beak it was heavy with marrow.
    Is that the wind dying? O no;
    It's only two devils, that blow
Through a murderer's bones, to and fro,
        In the ghost's moonshine.

4. THE GREAT INNOVATOR

He that will not apply new remedies must expect new evils; for time is the greatest innovator.

5. QUEEN MAB

O! then, I see, Queen Mab hath been with you . . .
She is the fairies' midwife, and she comes
In shape no bigger than an agate-stone
On the forefinger of an alderman,
Drawn with a team of little atomies
Athwart men's noses as they lie asleep.

6. THE MANTLE

If you have tears, prepare to shed them now.
You all do know this mantle; I remember
The first time ever Caesar put it on;

7. DESPAIR

O! that this too too solid flesh would melt,
Thaw, and resolve itself into a dew;
Or that the Everlasting had not fix'd
His canon 'gainst self-slaughter! O God! O God!
How weary, stale, flat and unprofitable
Seem to me all the uses of this world.

8. SHE WALKS IN BEAUTY

She walks in beauty, like the night
   Of cloudless climes and starry skies;
And all that's best of dark and bright
   Meet in her aspect and her eyes:
Thus mellow'd to that tender light
   Which heaven to gaudy day denies.

I revere the memory of Mr. F. as an estimable man and most indulgent husband, only necessary to mention Asparagus and it appeared or to hint at any little delicate thing to drink and it came like magic in a pint pottle, it was not ecstasy, but it was comfort.

10. A RED RED ROSE

O, my Luve's like a red red rose
  That's newly sprung in June;
Oh, my Luve's like the melodie
  That's sweetly play'd in tune.

★

1. MIZPAH

Mizpah; for he said, The Lord watch between me
and thee, when we are absent one from another.

2. VOYAGERS

The Owl and the Pussy-Cat went to sea
In a beautiful pea-green boat.

3. NEW YEAR'S EVE

Ring out the old, ring in the new,
Ring, happy bells, across the snow;
The year is going, let him go;
Ring out the false, ring in the true.

4. AUTUMNAL LEAVES

Thick as autumnal leaves that strow the brooks
In Vallombrosa, where th' Etrurian shades
High over-arch'd imbower.

5. EPITAPH

Under the wide and starry sky
Dig the grave and let me lie.
Glad did I live and gladly die,
And I laid me down with a will.

This be the verse you grave for me:
"Here he lies where he longed to be;
Home is the sailor, home from the sea,
    And the hunter home from the hill."

6.   ECHO

Sweet Echo, sweetest nymph, that liv'st unseen
    Within thy airy shell
By slow Meander's margent green,
    And in the violet-embroidered vale.

7.   FOR TO ADMIRE

For to admire an' for to see,
For to be 'old this world so wide
It never done no good to me,
But I can't drop it if I tried!

8.   COMMENT

Can storied urn or animated bust
    Back to its mansion call the fleeting breath?
Can honour's voice provoke the silent dust,
    Or flatt'ry soothe the dull, cold ear of death?

9.   THE PILGRIM

Who would true valour see,
    Let him come hither;

One here will constant be,
        Come wind, come weather.
There's no discouragement
Shall make him once relent
His first avow'd intent
        To be a pilgrim.

10. THE CITY

Well then; I now do plainly see
This busy world and I shall ne'er agree;
The very honey of all earthly joy
Does of all meats the soonest cloy,
        And they (methinks) deserve my pity,
Who for it can endure the stings,
The crowd, and buzz, and murmurings
        Of this great hive, the city.

★

1. ALL IS VANITY

Vanity of vanities, saith the Preacher, vanity of vanities; all is vanity.

What profit hath a man of all his labour which he taketh under the sun?

One generation passeth away, and another generation cometh.

2. WORTH WHILE

That best portion of a good man's life,
His little, nameless, unremembered acts
Of kindness and of love.

3. ACTION

Yet all experience is an arch wherethro'
Gleams that untravell'd world, whose margin fades
For ever and for ever when I move.
How dull it is to pause, to make an end,
To rust unburnish'd, not to shine in use!
As tho' to breathe were life. Life piled on life
Were all too little, and of one to me
Little remains: but every hour is saved
From that eternal silence, something more,
A bringer of new things.

4. THE MARTLET

This guest of summer,
The temple-haunting martlet, does approve
By his lov'd mansionry that the heaven's breath
Smells wooingly here; no jutty, frieze,
Buttress, nor coign of vantage, but this bird
Hath made his pendent bed and procreant cradle:
Where they most breed and haunt, I have observ'd,
The air is delicate.

5. AT REST

Sleep after toil, port after stormy seas,
Ease after war, death after life does greatly please.

6. HOPE

Hope springs eternal in the human breast;
Man never is, but always to be blessed.
The soul, uneasy, and confined from home,
Rests, and expatiates in a life to come.
Lo, the poor Indian! whose untutored mind
Sees God in clouds, or hears him in the wind;
His soul proud science never taught to stray
Far as the solar walk of milky way;
Yet simple nature to his hope has giv'n,
Behind the cloud-topped hill, an humbler heav'n.

7. THE MURDERESS

Come you spirits
That tend on mortal thoughts! unsex me here,
And fill me from the crown to the toe top full
Of direst cruelty; make thick my blood,
Stop up the access and passage to remorse,
That no compunctious visitings of nature
Shake my fell purpose, nor keep peace between
The effect and it!

8. LEST WE FORGET

The tumult and the shouting dies;
The Captains and the Kings depart:
Still stands Thine ancient sacrifice,
An humble and a contrite heart.
Lord God of Hosts, be with us yet,
Lest we forget—lest we forget.

9. COME

Come live with me, and be my love,
And we will some new pleasures prove
Of golden sands and crystal brooks,
With silken lines and silver hooks.

10. NOT VALUE FOR MONEY

The public buys its opinions as it buys its meat, or
takes in its milk, on the principle that it is cheaper to
do this than to keep a cow. So it is, but the milk is
more likely to be watered.

*

1   WIDE THE GATE

Wide is the gate and broad is the way that leadeth
to destruction, and many there be that go in thereat.

2.   LOVE

Yonder a maid and her wight
    Come whispering by;
War's annals will cloud into night
    Ere their story die.

3.   IN THE SPRING

In the Spring a livelier iris changes on the burnish'd
   dove;
In the Spring a young man's fancy lightly turns to
   thoughts of love.

4.   OVERGROWN

Wise nature did never put her precious jewels into
a garret four stories high; and therefore . . .
exceeding tall men had ever very empty heads.

5.   IGNOMINY

I am not so much afraid of death, as ashamed
thereof; 'tis the very disgrace and ignominy of our
natures.

6. AMBITION

Why, man, he doth bestride the narrow world
Like a Colossus; and we petty men
Walk under his huge legs, and peep about
To find ourselves dishonourable graves.
Men at some time are masters of their fates;
The fault, dear Brutus, is not in our stars,
But in ourselves, that we are underlings.

7. THE END IS DUST

Fear no more the lightning flash,
    Nor the all-dreaded thunder-stone;
Fear not slander, censure rash;
    Thou has finish'd joy and moan:
All lovers young, all lovers must
Consign to thee, and come to dust.

8. PUT THAT IN

Jenny kissed me when we met,
Jumping from the chair she sat in;
Time, you thief, who love to get
Sweets into your list, put that in:
Say I'm weary, say I'm sad,
Say that health and wealth have missed me,
Say I'm growing old, but add,
Jenny kissed me.

9. TIME TO STARE

What is this life if, full of care,
We have no time to stand and stare?

10. SWEET AFTON

Flow gently, sweet Afton, among thy green braes,
Flow gently, I'll sing thee a song in thy praise.
My Mary's asleep by thy murmuring stream,
Flow gently, sweet Afton, disturb not her dream.

★

1. SOFT ANSWER

A soft answer turneth away wrath.

2. INFINITUDE

Whether we be young or old,
Our destiny, our being's heart and home,
Is with infinitude, and only there;
With hope it is, hope that can never die,
Effort, and expectation, and desire,
And something evermore about to be.

3. THESE THREE

Self-reverence, self-knowledge, self-control,
These three alone lead life to sovereign power.

4. FRENZY

The lunatic, the lover, and the poet,
Are of imagination all compact:
One sees more devils than vast hell can hold,
That is, the madman; the lover, all as frantic,
Sees Helen's beauty in a brow of Egypt:
The poet's eye, in a fine frenzy rolling,
Doth glance from heaven to earth, from earth to
  heaven;

And, as imagination bodies forth
The forms of things unknown, the poet's pen
Turns them to shapes, and gives to airy nothing
A local habitation and a name.

5. THE VICTIM

Come away, come away, death,
   And in sad cypress let me be laid;
Fly away, fly away, breath:
   I am slain by a fair cruel maid.
My shroud of white, stuck all with yew,
   O! prepare it.
My part of death no one so true
   Did share it.

6. HELEN

Helen, they beauty is to me
   Like those Nicean barks of yore,
That gentle, o'er a perfumed sea,
   The weary, wayworn wanderer bore
   To his own native shore.

On desperate seas long wont to roam,
   Thy hyacinth hair, thy classic face,
Thy Naiad airs have brought me home
   To the glory that was Greece
   And the grandeur that was Rome.

7. THE STAGE

All the world's a stage,
And all the men and women merely players:
They have their exits and their entrances;
And one man in his time plays many parts.

8. THE QUEEN

The Queen was in her chamber, her sins were on her
    head.
She looked the spirits up and down and statelily she
    said:—
"Backwards and forwards and sideways though I've
    been,
Yet I am Harry's daughter and I am England's Queen!"

9. THE SNOB

Every day when he looked into the glass, and gave
the last touch to his consummate toilette, he offered
his grateful thanks to Providence that his family was
not unworthy of him.

10. WHAT SOME BELIEVE

The souls of women are so small,
That some believe they've none at all.

1   THE WORLD WITHOUT

Raging waves of the sea, foaming out their own
shame; wandering stars, to whom is reserved the
blackness of darkness for ever.

2.   APPARITION

She was a phantom of delight
When first she gleamed upon my sight;
A lovely apparition sent
To be a moment's ornament.

3.   HAPPY DAYS

Tears, idle tears, I know not what they mean,
Tears from the depth of some divine despair
Rise in the heart, and gather to the eyes,
In looking on the happy Autumn-fields,
And thinking of the days that are no more.

4.   THE MASTER

Others abide our question. Thou art free.
We ask and ask: Thou smilest and art still,
Out-topping knowledge.

5. STRENGTH

To suffer woes which Hope thinks infinite;
To forgive wrongs darker than death or night;
    To defy Power, which seems omnipotent;
To love, and bear; to hope till Hope creates
From its own wreck the thing it contemplates;
    Neither to change, nor falter, nor repent;
This, like thy glory, Titan, is to be
Good, great and joyous, beautiful and free;
This is alone Life, Joy, Empire, and Victory.

6. OUTCAST

They looking back, all th' eastern side beheld
Of Paradise, so late their happy seat,
Wav'd over by that flaming brand, the Gate
With dreadful faces throng'd and fiery arms.
Some natural tears they dropped, but wiped them
    soon;
The world was all before them, where to choose
Their place of rest, and Providence their guide:
They hand in hand with wandering steps and slow
Through Eden took their solitary way.

7. THE GOAL

I shall not be satisfied unless I produce something
which shall for a few days supersede the last fashionable
novel on the tables of young ladies.

8. BOOKS

In books lies the soul of the whole Past Time; the articulate audible voice of the Past, when the body and material substance of it has altogether vanished like a dream.

9. THE GROCER

The righteous minds of innkeepers
   Induce them now and then
To crack a bottle with a friend
   Or treat unmoneyed men,

But who hath seen the Grocer
   Treat housemaids to his teas
Or crack a bottle of fish-sauce
   Or stand a man a cheese?

10. RENEGADE

Just for a handful of silver he left us,
   Just for a riband to stick in his coat.

★

1.   CAN HE?

Can the Ethiopean change his skin, or the leopard his spots?

2.   WE ARE WONDERFUL

We carry within us the wonders, we seek without us. There is all Africa, and her prodigies in us.

3.   STEPPING STONES

I held it truth, with him who sings
    To one clear harp in divers tones,
    That men may rise on stepping-stones
Of their dead selves to higher things.

4.   THE CASE FOR MONARCHY

The characteristic of the English Monarchy is that it retains the feelings by which the heroic kings governed their rude age, and has added the feelings by which the constitutions of later Greece ruled in more refined ages.

5.   THE LINNET

I heard a linnet courting
His lady in the spring;

His mates were idly sporting,
  Nor stayed to hear him sing
    His song of love.
  I fear my speech distorting
    His tender love.

6. BOW-WOW

The Big Bow-Wow strain I can do myself like any
now going; but the exquisite touch, which renders
ordinary commonplace things and characters interest-
ing, from the truth of the description and the senti-
ment, is denied to me.

7. THE OATH OF LARS PORSENA

Lars Porsena of Clusium
  By the nine gods he swore
That the great house of Tarquin
  Should suffer wrong no more.
By the Nine Gods he swore it,
  And named a trysting day,
And bade his messengers ride forth,
East and west and south and north,
  To summon his array.

8. THE CHERRY

Now, of my three score years and ten,
Twenty will not come again;

And take from seventy years a score,
It only leaves me fifty more.

And since to look at things in bloom
Fifty springs are little room,
About the woodlands I will go
To see the cherry hung with snow.

9.   THE WHITE HORSE

Before the gods that made the gods
    Had seen their sunrise pass,
The White Horse of the White Horse Vale
    Was cut out of the grass.

10.   TOBACCO

Tobacco, divine, rare, superexcellent tobacco, which goes far beyond all their panaceas, potable gold, and philosopher's stones, a sovereign remedy to all diseases . . . But, as it is commonly abused by most men, which take it as tinkers do ale, 'tis a plague, a mischief, a violent purger of goods, lands, health, hellish, devilish, and damned tobacco, the ruin and overthrow of body and soul.

1. THROUGH A GLASS, DARKLY

When I was a child, I spake as a child, I understood as a child, I thought as a child: but when I became a man, I put away childish things. For now we see through a glass, darkly, but then face to face; now I know in part; but then shall I know even as also I am known.

2. EXILED

I travelled among unknown men
   In lands beyond the sea;
Nor England! did I know till then
   What love I bore to thee.

3. MAY DAY

You must wake and call me early, call me early,
   mother dear;
To-morrow 'ill be the happiest time of all the glad
   New-year;
Of all the glad New-year, mother, the maddest
   merriest day;
For I'm to be Queen o' the May, mother, I'm to be
   Queen o' the May.

4. DILEMMA

An unhappy alternative is before you, Elizabeth. From this day you must be a stranger to one of your parents. Your mother will never see you again if you do NOT marry Mr. Collins, and I will never see you again if you DO.

5. LONDON

Oh, London is a fine town,
    A very famous city,
Where all the streets are paved with gold,
    And all the maidens pretty.

6. LET'S AWAY

Come, let's away to prison;
We two alone will sing like birds i' the cage:
When thou dost ask me blessing, I'll kneel down,
And ask of thee forgiveness: and we'll live,
And pray, and sing, and tell old tales, and laugh
At gilded butterflies, and hear poor rogues
Talk of court news; and we'll talk with them too.

7. MELODIES

Heard melodies are sweet, but those unheard
Are sweeter; therefore, ye soft pipes, play on;
Not to the sensual ear, but, more endear'd,
Pipe to the spirit ditties of no tone.

8. LIVERPOOL

The folk that live in Liverpool, their heart is in their
  boots;
They go to hell like lambs, they do, because the
  hooter hoots.

9. LAMENT

I've heard them lilting, at the ewe milking.
  Lasses a' lilting, before dawn of day;
But now they are moaning, on ilka green loaning;
  The flowers of the forest are a' wede awae.

10. TO SEE OURSELS

O wad some Pow'r the giftie gie us
To see oursels as others see us!
It wad frae mony a blunder free us,
  And foolish notion.

1.   THE IMMORTAL SPIRIT

Dust as we are, the immortal spirit grows
Like harmony in music; there is a dark
Inscrutable workmanship that reconciles
Discordant elements, makes them cling together
In one society.

2.   DUTY

Not once or twice in our rough island-story,
The path of duty was the way to glory.

3.   THE FOUNDATIONS OF KNOWLEDGE

Hebraism and Hellenism—between these two
points of influence moves our World . . . Hebraism
and Hellenism are, neither of them, the law of human
development . . . they are, each of them, contributions to human development.

4.   TWO WHO MATTERED

You will see Coleridge—he who sits obscure
In the exceeding lustre and the pure
Intense irradiation of a mind,
Which, through its own internal lightning blind,
Flags wearily through darkness and despair—
A cloud-encircled meteor of the air,
A hooded eagle among blinking owls.

You will see Hunt—one of those happy souls
Which are the salt of the earth, and without whom
This world would smell like what it is—a tomb.

5. SATAN ENTHRONED

High on a throne of royal state, which far
Outshone the wealth of Ormus and of Ind,
Or where the gorgeous East with richest hand
Showers on her kings barbaric pearl and gold,
Satan exalted sat, by merit raised
To that bad eminence; and from despair
Thus high uplifted beyond hope.

6. RAPTURE

Darkling I listen; and, for many a time
I have been half in love with easeful Death,
Call'd him soft names in many a mused rhyme,
To take into the air my quiet breath;
Now more than ever seems it rich to die,
To cease upon the midnight with no pain.

7. DAUGHTERS OF TIME

Daughters of Time, the hypocritic Days,
Muffled and dumb like barefoot dervishes
And marching single in an endless file,
Bring diadems and faggots in their hands.
To each they offer gifts after his will—
Bread, kingdoms, stars and sky that holds them all

I, in my pleached garden, watch'd the pomp,
Forgot my morning wishes, hastily
Took a few herbs and apples, and the Day
Turn'd and departed silent. I, too late,
Under her solemn fillet saw the scorn.

8. THE LAND IS BRIGHT

For while the tired waves, vainly breaking,
   Seem here no painful inch to gain,
Far back, through creeks and inlets making,
   Comes silent, flooding in, the main.

And not by eastern windows only,
   When daylight comes, comes in the light,
In front, the sun climbs slow, how slowly,
   But westward, look, the land is bright.

9. PARODY

When fishes flew and forests walked
   And figs grew upon thorn,
Some moment when the moon was blood
   Then surely I was born.

With monstrous head and sickening cry
   And ears like errant wings,
The devil's walking parody
   Of all four-footed things.

I may not here omit those two main plagues, and common dotages of human kind, wine and women, which have infatuated and besotted myriads of people. They go commonly together.

ANSWERS

*

GROUP I, PAGE 1

1. Robert Browning: *Pippa Passes.*
2. Francis Bacon: *Apothegms.*
3. Edward Young: *The Complaint: Night Thoughts.*
4. Edmund Burke: *Reflections on the Revolution in France.*
5. William Congreve: *Letter to Dennis, concerning Humour in Comedy.*
6. Percy Bysshe Shelley: *Adonais.*
7. Thomas Gray: *Ode on a Distant Prospect of Eton College.*
8. George Meredith: *Love in the Valley.*
9. William Shakespeare: *Cymbeline.*
10. Alfred, Lord Tennyson: *Crossing the Bar.*

GROUP II, PAGE 4

1. Percy Bysshe Shelley: *Hellas.*
2. William Shakespeare: *Twelfth Night.*
3. William Blake: *Ah, Sun-Flower!*
4. Dante Gabriel Rossetti: *The Blessed Damozel.*
5. Sir Walter A. Raleigh: *Laughter from a Cloud: Wishes of an Elderly Man.*
6. John Keats: *Ode to a Nightingale.*
7. Oliver Goldsmith: *The Vicar of Wakefield.*
8. Robert Browning: *De Gustibus.*
9. George Bernard Shaw: *Candida.*
10. Ernest Dowson: *Non Sum Qualis Eram.*

GROUP III, PAGE 7

1. Robert Browning: *Home Thoughts from the Sea.*
2. William Butler Yeats: *The Lake Isle of Innisfree.*
3. George Bernard Shaw: *Arms and the Man.*
4. John Addington
      Symonds: *Hymn.*
5. Sir Henry John
      Newbolt: *Drake's Drum.*
6. Samuel Johnson: *Life of Johnson—Boswell.*
7. Samuel Taylor
      Coleridge: *Names.*
8. Elizabeth Barrett
      Browning: *Wine of Cyprus.*
9. Henry Wadsworth
      Longfellow: *A Psalm of Life.*
10. William Shakespeare: *As You Like It.*

GROUP IV, PAGE 10

1. Arthur William Edgar
      O'Shaughnessy: *Ode: "We are the Music
                                    Makers".*

2. Benjamin Disraeli: *The Young Duke.*
3. James Thomson: *Alfred: a Masque 1740.*
4. John Masefield: *Sea Fever.*
5. William Shakespeare: *Sonnets.*
6. Rupert Brooke: *The Dead.*
7. William Shakespeare: *Hamlet.*
8. Edward FitzGerald: *Omar Khayyam.*
9. Lewis Carroll: *Alice in Wonderland.*
10. Julia Ward Howe: *Battle Hymn of the American
                                Republic.*

1. The Holy Bible: *Book of Genesis.*
2. William Collins: *Ode Written in the Year 1746.*
3. George Meredith: *The Ordeal of Richard Feverel.*
4. William Shakespeare: *King Henry IV, Part I.*
5. William Shakespeare: *Sonnet.*
6. Robert Herrick: *To Electra.*
7. Lewis Carroll: *Alice Through the Looking-Glass.*
8. Robert Browning: *Caliban upon Setebos.*
9. Izaak Walton: *Compleat Angler.*
10. Elizabeth Barrett Browning: *A Musical Instrument.*

1. The Holy Bible: *Book of Numbers.*
2. Michael Drayton: *The Barons' Wars.*
3. Walt Whitman: *Out of the Cradle Endlessly Rocking.*
4. John Milton: *Comus.*
5. William Shakespeare: *King Henry V.*
6. George Bernard Shaw: *Heartbreak House.*
7. William Shakespeare: *As You Like It.*
8. Oliver Wendell Holmes: *The Chambered Nautilus: The Autocrat of the Breakfast Table.*
9. Lewis Carroll: *Alice Through the Looking-Glass.*
10. Robert Browning: *Apparent Failure.*

1. The Holy Bible: *Book of Judges.*
2. Edward Fitzgerald: *Omar Khayyam.*
3. John Greenleaf
   Whittier: *Maud Muller.*
4. John Milton: *Lycidas.*
5. William Shakespeare: *Othello.*
6. Joseph Addison: *The Tatler.*
7. William Shakespeare: *As You Like It.*
8. Alfred Edward
   Housman: *Epitaph on an Army of*
   Mercenaries.
9. Robert Herrick: *The Night Piece: To Julia.*
10. Sir Thomas Browne: *Religio Medici.*

1. The Holy Bible: *First Book of Kings.*
2. Thomas Hardy: *The Oxen.*
3. Oscar Wilde: *Importance of Being Earnest.*
4. Walter Horatio Pater: *The Renaissance: Leonardo da*
   Vinci.
5. William Blake: *Jerusalem.*
6. Percy Bysshe Shelley: *To a Skylark.*
7. William Shakespeare: *Macbeth.*
8. John Keats: *On First Looking into Chapman's*
   Homer.
9. Ralph Hodgson: *The Bells of Heaven.*
10. Elizabeth Barrett
    Browning: *Rime of the Duchess May.*

1. The Holy Bible: *Book of Proverbs.*
2. Benjamin Jonson: *A Pindaric Ode on the Death of Sir H. Morison.*
3. William Wordsworth: *Ode to Duty.*
4. Samuel Pepys: *Diary.*
5. Rev. Richard Harris Barham: *The Cynotaph.*
6. Richard Brinsley Sheridan: *The School for Scandal.*
7. George Meredith: *Diana of the Crossways.*
8. Charles Kingsley: *A Farewell.*
9. The Earl of Chesterfield: *Letter to his Son.*
10. Benjamin Disraeli: *Coningsby.*

1. The Holy Bible: *Book of Proverbs.*
2. Christopher Marlowe: *Faustus.*
3. William Wordsworth: *Ode: Intimations of Immortality.*
4. Alexander Pope: *Essay on Criticism.*
5. Hilaire Belloc: *The Tiger.*
6. Robert Southey: *The Old Man's Comforts, and how he Gained Them.*
7. George Peele: *Polyhymnia, Sonnet ad finem. A Farewell to Arms.*
8. Rudyard Kipling: *Cells.*
9. The Earl of Chesterfield: *Letter to his Son.*
10. Charles Dickens: *Our Mutual Friend.*

GROUP XIII, PAGE 39

1. The Holy Bible: *St. Matthew.*
2. Henry Wadsworth
   Longfellow: *My Lost Youth.*
3. Izaak Walton: *Compleat Angler: Epistle to the Reader.*
4. James Matthew Barrie: *What Every Woman Knows.*
5. Jane Austen: *Northanger Abbey.*
6. William Blake: *The Tiger.*
7. William Shakespeare: *Hamlet.*
8. Samuel Johnson: *Life of Johnson: Boswell.*
9. Ralph Waldo Emerson: *New England Reformers.*
10. Ralph Waldo Emerson: *Self-Reliance.*

GROUP XIV, PAGE 42

1. The Holy Bible: *Epistle of St. Paul to the Ephesians.*
2. Lewis Carroll: *The Walrus and the Carpenter.*
3. Charles Wolfe: *The Burial of Sir John Moore at Corunna.*
4. William Shakespeare: *The Merchant of Venice.*
5. Matthew Arnold: *In Memory of the Author of Obermann.*
6. Robert Louis
   Stevenson: *Songs of Travel.*
7. Sir Walter Scott: *Rokeby.*
8. John Gay: *The Beggar's Opera.*
9. Charles Dickens: *The Old Curiosity Shop.*
10. Lord Byron: *Don Juan.*

1. Edmund Burke: *Impeachment of Warren Hastings.*
2. Francis Thompson: *The Kingdom of God.*
3. Joseph Addison: *Cato.*
4. Francis Bacon: *Advancement of Learning.*
5. Algernon Charles
  Swinburne: *Erotion.*
6. William Shakespeare: *Hamlet.*
7. Edward Gibbon: *Autobiography.*
8. Walter de la Mare: *Epitaph.*
9. John Dryden: *Essay of Dramatic Poesy.*
10. The Holy Bible: *Isaiah.*

GROUP XVI, PAGE 48

1. The Holy Bible: *Epistle of St. Paul to the Romans.*
2. John Donne: *Song.*
3. Ella Wheeler Wilcox: *Solitude.*
4. William Shakespeare: *Measure for Measure.*
5. John Ruskin: *Unto This Last.*
6. William Schwenk
  Gilbert: *Patience.*
7. Charles Stuart
  Calverley: *Ballad.*
8. Samuel Butler: *Note Books: A Luxurious Death.*
9. Matthew Arnold: *The Forsaken Merman.*
10. The Holy Bible: *Isaiah.*

Group XXV, page 75

1. The Holy Bible: *The Book of Proverbs.*
2. William Wordsworth: *My Heart Leaps Up.*
3. Alfred, Lord Tennyson: *Ode on the Death of the Duke of Wellington.*
4. William Shakespeare: *The Merchant of Venice.*
5. William Shakespeare: *The Tempest.*
6. Samuel Pepys: *Diary.*
7. William Shakespeare: *Antony and Cleopatra.*
8. Walter Savage Landor: *Finis.*
9. Charles Dickens: *A Tale of Two Cities.*
10. Robert Browning: *Home Thoughts from Abroad.*

Group XXVI, page 78

1. The Holy Bible: *Book of Ruth.*
2. Alfred, Lord Tennyson: *Maud.*
3. William Shakespeare: *Macbeth.*
4. Sir Thomas Browne: *Religio Medici.*
5. John Milton: *Lycidas.*
6. Charles Lamb: *Essays of Elia: Mrs. Battle's Opinions on Whist.*
7. Richard Lovelace: *To Althea: From Prison.*
8. William Cowper: *John Gilpin.*
9. Robert Browning: *Parting at Morning.*
10. Francis Mahony: *The Bells of Shandon.*

Group XXVII, page 82

1. The Holy Bible: *The Book of Judges.*
2. John Masefield: *Beauty.*
3. John Stuart Mill: *Liberty.*
4. William Shakespeare: *Macbeth.*
5. Rupert Brooke: *The Soldier.*
6. John Milton: *L' Allegro.*
7. Rudyard Kipling: *Our Lady of the Snows.*
8. Thomas Babington Macaulay: *Lays of Ancient Rome: Horatius.*
9. William Congreve: *The Way of the World.*
10. Robert Browning: *Summum Bonum.*

Group XXVIII, page 85

1. The Holy Bible: *Book of Isaiah.*
2. William Butler Yeats: *When You are Old.*
3. Alfred, Lord Tennyson: *The Passing of Arthur.*
4. William Blake: *Book of Thel.*
5. Francis William Bourdillon: *Light.*
6. Sir Walter Scott: *The Lay of the Last Minstrel.*
7. Edward Lear: *Nonsense Songs: The Jumblies.*
8. Oliver Goldsmith: *Song: From the Vicar of Wakefield.*
9. Lewis Carroll: *Hunting of the Snark.*
10. William Shakespeare: *King Henry VIII.*

1. The Holy Bible   *The Song of Solomon.*
2. William Wordsworth.   *Sonnet: Composed on Westminster Bridge.*
3. Francis Thompson: *The Hound of Heaven.*
4. William Shakespeare: *The Merchant of Venice.*
5. Henry St. John, Viscount Bolingbroke: *On the Study of History.*
6. Sir Walter Raleigh: *The Passionate Man's Pilgrimage.*
7. Samuel Johnson: *Life of Johnson: Boswell.*
8. Oliver Goldsmith: *The Deserted Village*
9. Lewis Carroll: *Alice Through the Looking-Glass.*
10. Lord Byron: *Childe Harold.*

1. The Holy Bible: *Epistle of St. Paul to the Romans.*
2. Thomas Hood: *I Remember.*
3. Alfred, Lord Tennyson: *Maud.*
4. Francis Bacon: *Essays: Of Truth.*
5. Edmund Spenser: *The Faerie Queene.*
6. John Milton: *Hymn: On the Morning of Christ's Nativity*
7. John Keats: *La Belle Dame Sans Merci.*
8. Thomas Campbell: *Ye Mariners of England.*
9. John Dryden: *Lines Under Portrait of Milton.*
10. Robert Burns: *Bonnie Lesley.*

1. William Ernest Henley: *For England's Sake: Pro Rege Nostro.*
2. William Wordsworth *Lines Composed a Few Miles above Tintern Abbey.*
3. Alfred, Lord Tennyson: *Ulysses.*
4. William Shakespeare: *The Two Gentlemen of Verona.*
5. Percy Bysshe Shelley: *To Night.*
6. John Milton: *Areopagitica.*
7. Andrew Marvell: *Nymph Complaining for the Death of her Faun.*
8. Samuel Taylor Coleridge: *The Ancient Mariner.*
9. Charles Dickens: *Martin Chuzzlewit.*
10. Robert Browning: *A Grammarian's Funeral.*

GROUP XXXII, PAGE 98

1. The Holy Bible: *St. John's Gospel.*
2. Abraham Lincoln: *Words in a speech at Clinton. (Also attributed to Phineas Barnum.)*
3. Thomas Lovell Beddoes: *Wolfram's Song.*
4. Francis Bacon: *Essays: On Innovations.*
5. William Shakespeare: *Romeo and Juliet.*
6. William Shakespeare: *Julius Caesar.*
7. William Shakespeare: *Hamlet.*
8. Lord Byron: *Hebrew Melodies: She Walks in Beauty.*
9. Charles Dickens: *Little Dorrit.*
10. Robert Burns: *My Love is like a Red Red Rose.*

1. The Holy Bible: *Book of Genesis.*
2. Edward Lear: *Nonsense Songs: The Owl and the Pussy Cat.*
3. Alfred, Lord Tennyson: *In Memoriam.*
4. John Milton: *Paradise Lost.*
5. Robert Louis
        Stevenson: *Requiem.*
6. John Milton: *Comus.*
7. Rudyard Kipling: *For to Admire.*
8. Thomas Gray: *Elegy Written in a Country Churchyard.*
9. John Bunyan: *Pilgrim's Progress.*
10. Abraham Cowley: *The Mistress, or Love Verses.*

1. The Holy Bible: *Book of Ecclesiastes.*
2. William Wordsworth: *Lines Composed a Few Miles above Tintern Abbey.*
3. Alfred, Lord Tennyson: *Ulysses.*
4. William Shakespeare: *Macbeth.*
5. Edmund Spenser: *The Faerie Queene.*
6. Alexander Pópe: *An Essay on Man.*
7. William Shakespeare: *Macbeth.*
8. Rudyard Kipling: *Recessional.*
9. John Donne: *The Bait.*
10. Samuel Butler: *Material for a Projected Sequel to Alps and Sanctuaries. Public Opinion.*

1. The Holy Bible: *St. Matthew's Gospel.*
2. Thomas Hardy: *In Time of "The Breaking of Nations."*
3. Alfred, Lord Tennyson: *Locksley Hall.*
4. Francis Bacon: *Apothegms.*
5. Sir Thomas Browne: *Religio Medici.*
6. William Shakespeare: *Julius Caesar.*
7. William Shakespeare: *Cymbeline.*
8. James Henry Leigh
          Hunt: *Rondeau.*
9. William Henry Davies: *Leisure.*
10. Robert Burns: *Flow Gently, Sweet Afton.*

1. The Holy Bible: *Book of Proverbs.*
2. William Wordsworth: *The Prelude.*
3. Alfred, Lord Tennyson: *Œnone.*
4. William Shakespeare: *A Midsummer Night's Dream.*
5. William Shakespeare: *Twelfth Night.*
6. Edgar Allan Poe: *To Helen.*
7. William Shakespeare: *As You Like It.*
8. Rudyard Kipling: *The Looking-Glass.*
9. Benjamin Disraeli: *Lothair.*
10. Samuel Butler: *Miscellaneous Thoughts.*

1. The Holy Bible: *General Epistle of St. Jude.*
2. William Wordsworth: *She was a Phantom of Delight.*
3. Alfred, Lord Tennyson: *The Princess.*
4. Matthew Arnold: *Sonnet: Shakespeare.*
5. Percy Bysshe Shelley: *Prometheus Unbound.*
6. John Milton: *Paradise Lost.*
7. Thomas Babington
       Macaulay: *Trevelyan's Life and Letters of Macaulay.*
8. Thomas Carlyle: *Heroes and Hero-Worship. The Hero as Man of Letters.*
9. Gilbert Keith
       Chesterton: *Song Against Grocers.*
10. Robert Browning: *The Lost Leader.*

GROUP XXXVIII, PAGE 116

1. The Holy Bible: *Book of Isaiah.*
2. Sir Thomas Browne: *Religio Medici.*
3. Alfred, Lord Tennyson: *In Memoriam.*
4. Walter Bagehot: *The English Constitution: The Monarchy.*
5. Robert Bridges: *I Heard a Linnet Courting.*
6. Sir Walter Scott: *Journal: On Jane Austen.*
7. Thomas Babington
       Macaulay: *Lays of Ancient Rome: Horatius.*
8. Alfred Edward
       Housman: *A Shropshire Lad.*
9. Gilbert Keith
       Chesterton: *Ballad of the White Horse.*
10. Robert Burton: *Anatomy of Melancholy.*

1. The Holy Bible: *First Epistle of St. Paul to the Corinthians.*
2. William Wordsworth: *I Travelled Among Unknown Men.*
3. Alfred, Lord Tennyson: *The May Queen.*
4. Jane Austen: *Pride and Prejudice.*
5. George Coleman: *Heir-at-Law.*
6. William Shakespeare: *King Lear.*
7. John Keats: *Ode to a Grecian Urn.*
8. Gilbert Keith
   Chesterton: *Me Heart.*
9. Jane Elliot: *The Flowers of the Forest.*
10. Robert Burns: *To a Louse.*

1. William Wordsworth: *The Prelude.*
2. Alfred, Lord Tennyson: *Ode on the Death of the Duke of Wellington.*
3. Matthew Arnold: *Culture and Anarchy.*
4. Percy Bysshe Shelley: *Letter to Maria Gisborne.*
5. John Milton: *Paradise Lost.*
6. John Keats: *Ode to a Nightingale.*
7. Ralph Waldo Emerson: *Days.*
8. Arthur Hugh Clough: *Say Not, The Struggle Naught Availeth.*
9. Gilbert Keith
   Chesterton: *The Donkey.*
10. Robert Burton: *Anatomy of Melancholy.*

SOME
PENGUIN
PUBLICATIONS

PTARMIGAN BOOKS

ASK ME ANOTHER
Hubert Phillips
Fifty Quizzes of ten questions each, arranged for friendly competition. They cover a wide field of general knowledge, and demand mental agility as well.

SOMETHING TO THINK ABOUT
Hubert Phillips
A book of logical and mathematical problems to exercise your wits.

CHIPWINKLE
Hubert Phillips
A hundred crosswords from 'the literary remains of the late Eugene Chipwinkle,' a Victorian eccentric invented by the author. By some strange chance they have not been published before – but every crossword fan will enjoy them now, because they are different.

TRIPLETS
Beryl Cross and Hubert Phillips
Another Series of fifty Quizzes, but this time three answers are needed to each question. A serious test of your general knowledge as well as an agreeable pastime.

PLAYTIME
Hubert Phillips
Games of every kind – quiet and strenuous, indoor and outdoor, solitary and social, for the party and the fireside. Many forgotten favourites and a lot of new games as well.

TO TEST YOUR KNOWLEDGE
W. Norman Dixon and Margaret Dixon
Sixty Quizzes covering history, geography, science, art, politics, nature, sport, and other subjects.

TRAVEL . ADVENTURE
BIOGRAPHY

—

Two Years Before the Mast : *Richard Dana*
A voyage in sail round the Horn and back

Lord Anson's Voyage : *Edited A. W. C. Pack*
Chronicles of a famous British admiral

Pearls and Men : *Louis Kornitzer*
Something about pearl-diving, buying and selling

The Lawless Roads : *Graham Greene*
A journey in Mexico

The Best is Yet : *Morris Ernst*
The candid autobiography of a famous American
lawyer

Life Class : *Ludwig Bemelmans*
Sketches of life below stairs at the Hotel Splendide

Siren Land : *Norman Douglas*
A close-up of a classic corner of Italy

Alexander Pope : *Edith Sitwell*
A distinguished portrait of the great English satirist

African Discovery : *M. Perham and J. Simmons*
Passages from the annals of African exploration

The Smith of Smiths : *Hesketh Pearson*
An amusing life of Sydney Smith, the clerical wit

Nansen : *E. E. Reynolds*
An authoritative life of the great explorer

The Du Mauriers : *Daphne du Maurier*
An intimate biography of the famous Du Maurier
family

The Hero of Delhi : *Hesketh Pearson*
A soldier in India before and during the Mutiny

PELICAN BOOKS

This comprehensive series, most of the books in which are written specially for it, ranges over subjects as diverse as architecture and psychology, law and music, botany and physiology, archæology and philosophy. A selection of some recent and forthcoming titles is shown here.

* *a double volume*   ** *a special volume 2s. 6d.*

PENGUIN OCCASIONALS

These publications, appearing at irregular intervals, are intended for the reader desiring authoritative information on science, the arts, and contemporary affairs. Subscriptions for all of them are accepted by the publishers, Penguin Books Limited, Harmondsworth, Middlesex, at a rate of seven shillings post free for four issues of one book.

PENGUIN NEW WRITING

A collection of critical and creative writing. Its contributions are selected from the work of world-known writers, artists and new authors. Each issue contains sixteen pages of plates.

PENGUIN PARADE

Presents in an invigorating manner informative articles by authoritative writers on social and artistic affairs. The contents are varied, consisting of critical essays on the arts and social problems, short stories, poems and illustrations.

NEW BIOLOGY

A miscellany of essays summarising aspects of contemporary biological research and application. Each number has a sixteen-page inset of plates and a glossary explaining the scientific terms used in the text.

SCIENCE NEWS

Authoritative information on scientists and their work, compiled by experts for the student, teacher and the non-professional reader. Also contains line drawings and photogravure plates to illustrate the subjects treated.

PENGUIN FILM REVIEW

A publication devoted to up-to-the-minute film news and matters, surveying, in a progressive, stimulating manner, all the activities and influences of the film. Also contains thirty-two pages of illustrations from British and foreign films.

PENGUIN MUSIC MAGAZINE

Is intended to give the music lover information on the world of music and musicians. The articles, written by acknowledged authorities, are varied and controversial and each issue has thirty-two pages of illustrations.

One shilling and sixpence each